the DYING of the LIGHT

Living with Alzheimer's Disease

A Personal Journey
by Arthur Olson

The Staff of the Oak Bay Kiwanis Pavilion
Erna Shou Jacobs, RN, Administrator
Louise Johnson, RN, Director of Care
Alyson Hawksworth, RN
Irene Barnes, RN

GSPH

Published by

GSPH GENERAL STORE
PUBLISHING HOUSE INC.

1 Main Street Burnstown, Ontario, Canada K0J 1G0
Telephone (613) 432-7697 or (613) 432-9385

ISBN 0-919431-53-4

Printed and bound in Canada.

Designed by Leanne Enright
Cover illustration by Bill Slavin

Canadian Cataloguing in Publication Data

Olson, Arthur
    The Dying of the light: living with alzheimer's disease
ISBN 0-919431-53-4

    1. Olson, Arthur   2. Alzheimer's disease--Patients--Home care.
2. Alzheimer's disease--Patients--Family relationships.
3. Alzheimer's disease--Patients--Long-term care.   I. Title.

RC523.O47 1992   362.1'96831   C92-090206-5

First Printing August 1992

DEDICATION

This book is dedicated to our children, Ginny and Randy, for their support and caring, and to the staff of the Oak Bay Kiwanis Pavilion for the loving care they have given Aila.

A special thanks goes to Pat Chivers who typed the manuscript, gave advice and encouragement, and demonstrated, by her good humour, a love of life.

TABLE OF CONTENTS

INTRODUCTION

Dylan Thomas must have known Alzheimer's Disease when he wrote: "Do not go gentle into that good night" and "Rage, rage against the dying of the light."[1]

Anyone who has contact with the disease through loved ones knows the rage that is expressed both by the one afflicted and the survivors. The disease is truly a "dying of the light." It robs the afflicted ones of their powers to think, to communicate and to recognize those whom they have loved with great joy throughout their lives. To the survivors, it is a dream play—unreal. The stage is set, the acts are known and the ending is predetermined. The play begins, the house lights dim, but continue dimming throughout the play until the last scene is in darkness. And the rage grows.... The play is confusing but you dare not leave. You know the play will end, but you know not when. The rage and confusion grow until ambivalence, or perhaps resignation, ends in a dream state of unreality. This is Alzheimer's disease. We are all victims and we "rage against the dying of the light." It affects between 100,000 to 300,000 middle-aged Canadians and annually ranks as the fourth or fifth leading cause of death.

Alzheimer's is a disease of loss. Only a faint smile of recognition or the now infrequent, "Are you Arthur?" remains of the close and loving relationship that existed between my wife and me. Sometimes I wonder, as the nerves in the brain deteriorate and become increasingly entangled, if the mind is still intact although the brain is not. I don't want to get into a philosophical discussion but, are the mind and the brain the same thing? Are the smiles, the holding of hands and the feeling of warmth and contentment that exists between us a meeting of the minds? Perhaps how we view and care for the victims of Alzheimer's is based upon our concept of the mind and the brain. It certainly has made a difference to me.

In the early stages of Alzheimer's disease, there are only minor indications and hints of things to come: not remembering a fre-

[1] Thomas, Dylan. "Do not go into that good night."
J.M. Dent & Sons Ltd. 1984.

quently called telephone number or a conversation from the previous day. Later, the dying of the light may express itself in forgetting to prepare a meal or to think about tomorrow. Confusion in taking telephone messages is a frequent and frustrating experience for all family members.

The progression of the disease is as varied as the unique qualities and abilities of its victims. It may progress rapidly or slowly. It may be severely debilitating or it may express itself in moderate, more gentle dysfunctions. Commonly, there are rapid periods of decline followed by plateau periods of little change. It is also apparent that the younger the victim, the more rapid the decline, the shorter the plateau periods and the greater the disability. Thankfully for these people the battle is usually shorter.

As the disease progressed in my wife, Aila, I tried to express it to myself so that I could understand. After visiting her one day in the Oak Bay Kiwanis Pavilion, I wrote this for myself; perhaps it will help you to understand.

ARE YOU ARTHUR?

She sits by the window
Remembering — not quite,
With a smile,
   How are the children?
   It looks like rain.
   We started to ...
Would you like to take a walk?
   Where?
   I fed them today.
We haven't fed them yet.
   We must ...
   Tomorrow maybe.
   Are they happy?
   Happy — happy — happy
   I ate it.
   Do you live far away?
No my love.
   Are you my Arthur?

The purpose of this book is to take you with my wife and me through the stages of our journey with her battle with Alzheimer's disease. It will, I hope, help you to understand the progression of the disease, as well as the questions I asked and the information I received to aid in my understanding of the resources available as the disease progressed. Not all of the right questions were asked and so with the help of good friends and medical professionals, information is provided that might make your journey easier. The book is organized in the sequence of our experiences. I wish that the information had been available to Aila and me as we began the journey.

Chapter 1

CAUSES AND SYMPTOM IDENTIFICATION

I don't know when I first thought that something was wrong with Aila but as I think back I can remember little signs of a lapse of memory. We are a close family and as the children married, dispersed and gave us grandchildren, the telephone bills became larger and larger. Often the explanation from Aila was that she had forgotten to tell them something or that she didn't remember what they had said so she needed to call them again. Later, the telephone bills were hidden — whereabouts unknown. I usually went to the telephone-company office on the 20th of each month to get a copy of the bill and pay the account. I found a three-year-old bill last week when I turned the mattress in one of the spare bedrooms — no need to make a fuss.

As time progressed, other behaviour became noticeable. Aila frequently would not remember what we had eaten for supper the night before or what events had taken place the previous day. On one occasion when I took Aila to our family doctor for a check-up I mentioned to him my concern about her memory loss. He dismissed it as normal ageing.

The children became more concerned as time progressed because they found the repetition of questions and the lack of memory a great concern. The intellectually sharp, funny, warm, loving and open person they knew seemed to be ill and none of us knew why.

Overview Of Senile Dementia — Alzheimer Type

In medical reports the disease is often referred to as SDAT (Senile Dementia — Alzheimer Type). When I first saw this on a medical report my thought was that Aila isn't senile. She was not senile then and she is not senile now. She has Alzheimer's disease (a form of dementia) and it is unlike age-related senile dementia. I'm angry at the terms and sometimes I'm even angry at Dr. Alzheimer, even though I know he had nothing to do with causing the disease that bears his name. I wonder if Dr. Salk and Dr. Alzheimer have the same sense of pride in their discoveries.

Senility is an obvious loss of mental and physical control that is often accompanied by emotional problems. There may or may not be any physical damage to the brain, but in many cases the symptoms of senility may be minimized by medication and counselling. Alzheimer's disease is characterized by the death of brain tissue and the gradual deterioration of the brain neurons. It cannot be treated with any known medication and is progressive in nature.

Dr. Alois Alzheimer, in 1907, was the first to describe the physiological changes that present themselves as neurofibrillary tangles, abnormal twisted fibres inside neurons of the brain. The parts of the brain affected by the disease are those related to association, language, space orientation, higher cognitive functions, memory and emotions. Motor, sensory and visual problems occur later in the progression of the disease. The areas in which the tangles occur are called plaques, and the more tangles and plaques there are, the greater the impairment.

Alzheimer's disease affects about one in a hundred adults. It may appear as early as age forty but generally not before the mid-sixties.

At the present time, the cause of the disease is not known. It is incurable and irreversible.

The incidence of Alzheimer's disease increases with age. Approximately twenty per cent of the population over age eighty has the disease to some degree.

Alzheimer's disease is difficult to diagnose. The current misdiagnosis rate is ten to thirty per cent.

Five Theories Of Its Cause

Alzheimer's disease is not like hardening of the arteries nor it is contagious. Yet, something triggers the disease. Research has used all of its -ologies (i.e. virology, immunology) to discover the cause, but for the present, all we have are five possibilities.

Trace Metal Studies

Aluminium has been found in larger-than-normal concentrations in the neurofibrillary tangles of many Alzheimer's patients. It is unknown whether the deposits act as a toxin causing Alzheimer's disease or if the accumulation of aluminium is the result of other chemical changes in the body.

Neurochemical Studies

A major discovery in our understanding of the disease is related to the chemicals in the brain which allow sensory impulses to pass through the nervous system to the area of the brain where those impulses are translated into something we recognize or know. An enzyme needed to manufacture one of these chemical transmitters (acetylcholine) is deficient in Alzheimer's patients and therefore not enough acetylcholine is produced to allow the brain to function normally. Neurons using acetylcholine are especially prominent in the memory area of the brain. It is because of this that loss of short-term memory (the most recent events) is the first symptom of the disease.

Infectious Agents Studies

We probably know less about the possibility of a virus or bacterium being the cause of Alzheimer's disease than any other possible cause. Normal brain tissue exposed to extracts of Alzheimer's-infected brain tissue has developed nerve tangle fibres similar to those found in Alzheimer's disease. The difficulty in doing this kind of research is obvious. Animal studies with animals of similar brain construction must be done or human subjects must volunteer for a study.

Immunological Studies

A possible cause frequently mentioned relates to a general theory of ageing. The theory suggests that as the individual's biological clock ticks, the genes that control cell replacement and repair of minor damage to cell chromosomes become less effective and vital. Errors occur in the genetic code resulting in a slowing of the normal defences of the immune system and, in some cases, misinformation being sent through the cells of the body.

Genetic Studies

I left genetic studies until last because it included the question immediately raised by the children when they were told that their mother had Alzheimer's disease. I had a hard enough job dealing with my own pain but the pain of the children, I'm afraid, put me over the edge. I had to reassure them, comfort them and at the same time let them know that I was personally handling the situation. All I wanted was a Linus blanket and someone to tell me it was going to be OK. The last thing I needed was a group cry-in. I had to find the answer to their questions because, after all, I was the father, husband, and I was supposed to know.

There is no clear-cut evidence to support the idea that Alzheimer's disease is inherited although there is the possibility that rather than having one-in-a-hundred odds, the chances may increase to four-in-a-hundred odds if a close relative is afflicted. We are a composite, however, of all the genetic components of our ancestors. Look at your own family tree and determine your own odds. Geneticists suspect that there is a gene component to Alzheimer's, but several genes are involved that must interact spontaneously with some change in environmental factors to trigger the disease.

Although there is a possibility of five different areas of study in respect to the disease, the cause may be the result of the interaction of multiple factors. In other words, as with all things in life, things are not as simple, clear and organized as they appear to be.

The Tell-Tale Signs

The progression of Alzheimer's disease is usually slow and gradual. The changes are almost imperceptible and in a supportive family environment may be masked from other people for a considerable length of time. I am really not sure that I noticed much change in Aila in the beginning. In a long and happy marriage, it is not unusual for the partners to know the needs, moods, behaviour, and reactions of each other by instinct. No verbal communication is necessary and a glance or body posture will do. We anticipate each other as second nature without conscious effort or preplanning. It is not unusual, therefore, to be unaware of subtle changes. More abrupt and unusual changes in behaviour often come as a surprise.

Aila loved to read the news magazines, to discuss politics and to follow the dealings of the financial world. As the unread, untouched pile of magazines and newspapers began to grow, I became concerned for Aila's vision. We both went for examinations and were told that our vision was the same as at our last examination. Why then had Aila stopped doing the things that were of extreme interest to her for all of her adult life?

After Aila stopped reading altogether it became more difficult to control our social contacts so that neither she nor I felt uncomfortable. Our friends became concerned that Aila was not well and felt that, when we were all together, Aila wasn't really there or seemed to slip away in her thoughts.

During the summer of 1988 it became more obvious to our friends that something was wrong because Aila sat passively when we discussed politics. In earlier times, this was not a topic that Aila would avoid. It was something our group of friends always enjoyed talking about. Of course, our mutual agreement about likes, dislikes and personalities only enhanced our enjoyment.

On October 16, 1988, our dreams, plans and tranquillity came to a screeching halt. I was downstairs watching television and Aila had gone upstairs to the bedroom. I don't know where our dog was, probably on the bed waiting for us to turn in for the evening. I heard Aila coming down the stairs and looked up as she started to speak: "Why are we in this hotel? I don't like it. I want to go home. I want to sleep in my own bed."

Aila was afraid and insecure. I was afraid and insecure. It wasn't a very good combination for helping either one of us. All I could think of to do was to turn on all the lights and to go with her around the house pointing out the pictures of the children and grandchildren, the paintings she liked, while talking about when and the circumstances of how we had bought them. This seemed to quiet her down. We had a cup of hot cocoa and went to bed. It's amazing how old, familiar habits take over in a crisis when you don't know what to do.

The next morning Aila remembered nothing of the night before. The feeling that she was not in her own home, however, continued to return periodically until she went to the Oak Bay Kiwanis Pavilion. Sometimes our home was a motel, and at other times, the prison in Finland in which she was detained by the Germans for a short period of time during her early teens. These events were frightening for her and totally frustrating for me. There was nothing I could do but try to make her feel secure and try to divert her attention.

We went to see our family doctor the next afternoon and I related to him the events of the preceding evening. Aila told him that I wasn't her husband but rather a nice man that brought her to see him. The doctor and I decided that she should have a full blood and urine evaluation. He suggested a CT scan (computerized tomography). I also wanted Aila to have an EEG (electroencephalogram). The CT scan was used to show the extent of cortical atrophy while the EEG showed the functioning of the brain when exposed to varying stimuli. My reading and instincts told me that both were necessary if a diagnosis was going to be confirmed.

It was no more than ten days after the tests when our doctor called and said, "The results of the tests are compatible with patients who have been found to have Alzheimer's disease." I am sure that he also said other things but I don't think I was listening. I was stunned. I wanted to cry but I couldn't. I wanted to rage but I didn't dare. The first conscious thought I had was, Oh my God.

After the initial information had a chance to sink in, our doctor suggested that it would be appropriate to have a geriatrics specialist brought into the case for his analysis of the testing data, his examination for dementia and an ADL (activities of daily living) evaluation. His evaluation confirmed the diagnosis of Alzheimer's disease.

A person of normal or above-normal intellectual ability is expected to be able to retain facts, learn new things, remember recent events, have good judgement and be aware of his or her surroundings. A neurological examination is extremely important but psychological functioning is also important. It is a window into the world of the person infected with Alzheimer's disease. It is through this window that we can observe changes in the perceptions and awareness of the patient's perceived reality. Any changes in how the Alzheimer's patient perceives the world around them can be observed by checking specific functioning over a period of time at three to six-month intervals.

When Aila went for her examination the doctor asked a few everyday questions: "Who is the Premier of British Columbia?" "I don't know," she replied. "What season of the year is it?" She smiled and said, "Summer." (It was winter.) "What city do you live in?" "Helsinki." And so I sat listening, sinking deeper and deeper into a sense of hopelessness.

Later in the week, when the doctor and I talked, he indicated that he could not predict the rate of deterioration by one examination but would see her again in four months to do another assessment. Perhaps he could tell me more then. I asked him if it would help in his evaluation if I kept some notes of my observations over the period of the next several months. The following are observations that one can make at approximately three to four-week intervals. Observations should all be made during a three-day time period, and the responses recorded.

ORIENTATION

Place

1. What is the name of this city?
2. Where is the bathroom?
3. Where is the front door?
4. How do we get upstairs?

Time

1. What is today's date?
2. Is it morning or afternoon?
3. What month is it?
4. Look at the clock (not digital) and tell me the time.
5. Draw me a clock with hours on it and make it read 3:30.

Person

1. Who am I? What do I do?
2. What is your name?
3. What is the name of our dog/cat?
4. What is our son(s)/daughter(s)/name(s)?

Memory

Recent

1. What did we have for lunch/breakfast?
2. What did you see on television today?
3. When did we last see our son(s)?
4. When did you last talk to ____ on the phone?
5. What is the name of your best friend?

Retention

Digit span forward

1. Say these numbers after me, 721, 395, 648.

   (If the individual you are evaluating cannot do one of these, do not go on to #2.)
2. Say these numbers after me, 2851, 4635, 1627.

Digit span backward

1. Say these numbers *backwards* after me, 15, 21, 35.

   (If one of these cannot be done successfully, stop here.)

2. Count backwards from 100 to 80.

Object Span

1. Place five common objects on a table. Point to each object and ask the person to give its name. Cover the objects with a cloth and ask the person to name all the things they can remember.

2. Repeat the above with five different objects.

GENERAL INFORMATION

1. What animal does wool come from?

2. What do I need to make bread?

3. In what month is Christmas?

These and other general questions may be asked.

Obviously, you do not irritate a person with Alzheimer's disease by sitting her down and giving her this evaluation. You make the observations in an informal, even offhanded way. You stop when you notice the person becoming tired or inattentive. Other observations that might help you in understanding the progress of the disease and aid in the prognosis should also be recorded. Some examples of this type of observations from my diary are:

Our dog was sitting next to Aila but she asked, "Where is Sugar Ray?" (Obviously our dog is a boxer.)

Aila passed me on the stairs but didn't see me.

Aila looked all over the house for her mother. Aila's mother is eighty-five and lives in Helsinki, Finland.

I provided the doctor with the information that I had recorded, and with his second evaluation in June, he was able to estimate the progress of the disease. I was devastated. He told me that, in the near future, Aila would have to go into a facility for long-term care.

Chapter 2

THE STAGES OF ALZHEIMER'S DISEASE

The onset of Alzheimer's disease is like a cat walking on soft paws, unseen, unheard, very slow and gradual in its movements. Over a period of time, however, it becomes more rambunctious, progressively destructive and deteriorative. At first, what we observe in the Alzheimer's patient is often minor change that doesn't register as something of great concern. Gradually, however, the person tends to become more forgetful, especially about more recent events. The individual may forget to turn off the oven, may misplace or hide things, may have to recheck to see if something has been done and may take longer than usual with chores that were once done quickly. Aila, for example, would often vacuum the living room, dining room and kitchen floors three or four times a day because she had forgotten that she had already done it earlier.

As the disease progresses, problems in abstract thinking may be observed. The patient may become more confused, irritable, agitated, and may undergo what may be considered, by the caregiver, major personality changes. The ability to concentrate, to know where they themselves are, and to speak may also be affected.

It is not unusual in the latter stages for Alzheimer's victims to wander. I would often have to send out a brigade of kids on their bicycles to see if they could find my wife somewhere in the neighbourhood, to take her by the hand and to guide her back home. In the most severe stages, the disease renders its victims absolutely and totally incapable of caring for themselves.

The pattern of the progression of the disease, the severity and the sequence of changes that take place in neurological functioning as a result of Alzheimer's disease are as different as are the persons afflicted. We know that the symptoms are progressive but there are enormous variations in the progression of the disease itself, from one person to another. In some cases, there may be very rapid decline, but in most cases where the individuals afflicted are older (seventy plus) there may be many months when there is little change at all. Limitations in physical activities during the latter stages of the disease may cause the person to become less resistant to common illnesses such as pneumonia. Sometimes special types of cancers may develop along with infections that may significantly shorten life expectancy.

Although the people who are afflicted with Alzheimer's may have no idea why they behave as they do, or even that they do behave as they do, the changes in personality function observed by others will be of enormous concern to caregivers.

Stages of the Disease

Stage One

The first stage of Alzheimer's disease can be described as mild to moderate in its severity. It can be considered analogous to the ages of young adult and adolescence in normal development. Like young adults or adolescents, Alzheimer's patients have cognitive difficulty in dealing with employment or situations that demand attention to detail and to complex analysis. They may no longer know how to handle the problems of banking or balancing accounts. Certainly, anything that demands a great deal of planning would be beyond their failing abilities.

During this period of time, the most insidious loss is that of memory. The repetition of questions, the retelling of the same stories, the constant problem of meeting old experiences as if they were happening for the first time can be very wearing for the Alzheimer's patient and disconcerting for the caregiver.

Another concern during this first stage of development is that Alzheimer's patients must feel secure in their surroundings. An overnight visit away from home can bring on an anxiety attack as can the event of a primary caregiver being away for an evening. The constraints placed upon the caregiver are overwhelming. Are you willing to take the chance of your loved one having a major anxiety reaction or do you limit your activity so that you are immediately available and responsive should the situation occur? Because many anxiety attacks or periods of increased confusion occur in the evening, caregivers must determine which particular routines are most acceptable to them.

I have tried a number of different suggested solutions to the problem: have a friend sit with Aila, have the doctor prescribe a drug, bring her with me, or plan my activities so that I could be at home with Aila in the evening. The last became my solution, which may be no solution at all. However, it was the only one with which I felt comfortable.

It is important during this stage to anticipate, as best one can, the problems that may lead to greater anxiety. Aila was very concerned about her mother in Finland living alone in a condominium even though her mother had many relatives who would periodically call in to talk with her, or prepare her a meal and attend to her well-being. Aila frequently telephoned her mother. The problem was, however, that the next day she would have no recollection of the call and would want to call again. One of the most useful things I found in addressing this particular problem was to get an answering machine attached to the telephone. This would record any conversation that transpired. In this way I could always play back her mother's tape and say to her, "Remember, we called your mother yesterday; listen to the tape and you will know that she's all right."

The Alzheimer's patient needs familiar routine and familiar surroundings. It was important, if Aila was going to enjoy a video movie, that she have some idea of what was going to happen, and that there be something in the movie with which she'd had a previous enjoyable experience.

And so our life progressed.

It was a sad time but not an unhappy time. We talked about past events and the children, we laughed together, we fed the sea-gulls every day, visited the duck pond and watched our favourite, well-worn movies on the VCR. We held hands and walked, making the most of precious moments before the dying of the light.

In summary, what can I say about this first stage of Alzheimer's disease? We can observe, for example, that these people have less energy and less initiative and appear to have much slower reactions. In other words, they have less spontaneity and sparkle. They often have difficulty expressing themselves when in the past this presented no particular problem. They are much slower to learn new tasks. They want routine. They do not want new experiences because new experiences frighten them. They want to go places that they have been before and they want to do things that they have done before, over and over again. Sometimes they become very angry for no reason at all apparent. The caregiver must be aware of this and back off, go to another room, sit down, go to the kitchen, make a cup of coffee and then come back as if nothing has happened and try to steer the conversation in another direction.

Stage Two

The second stage may be described as moderately severe and approximates the developmental level of a child between four and six years of age. The patients need help with all those tasks discussed in the first stage. They also require additional help with bathing, dressing and in some cases cutting their food for eating. Alzheimer's patients, by this time, have lost some insight into the world around them and into how to deal with particular situations that arise from day to day. They may be concerned about their declining abilities but often are not if they have a supportive environment in which familiarity is consistent and where the caregiver gives a great deal of moral support. At this stage Alzheimer's patients begin to show marked personality changes. They tend to be insensitive to the feelings of others, not in a direct way but indirectly through their apparent withdrawal from what might have been very loving and caring relationships. They are also easy to anger and often manufacture reasons for their anger.

I can give you several examples. During this period of time Aila would frequently become very angry with the children, whom she had not seen for several months, because she believed that they had taken something from our home which, of course, they hadn't. She would either refuse to talk to them on the telephone, or if she did, she would do so in a very stern, sterile voice.

During this stage of the disease, it may also be necessary for the caregiver to have some help in the home to take care of the Alzheimer's patient. We were fortunate enough to have Joyce Spearman, a marvellously gentle, English lady, who would come and care for Aila six hours a day, five days per week. She had no previous experience with Alzheimer's patients but knew from her nursing experience that she was not dealing with senility. If Aila wished to vacuum the floor five times a day, that was fine with Joy. If she wanted to dust three or four times, fine, Joy was willing to dust. If she wished to go for a walk, Joy was willing to walk with her.

One of the incidents that happened at this period was the result of Aila's spontaneous anger. Joy was frequently the object of her anger because Joy was unknown — she was not familiar to Aila. Each morning when she saw Joy, it was a new experience; she did not remember from the day before that she had seen Joy. The situation became such that, if Joy went into the kitchen for four or five minutes to make tea, Aila would have forgotten her when she returned. Aila, for one reason or another, saw Joy as an intruder and would demand that she get out of the house. It was not infrequent that Joy would call me at work and say, "Aila kicked me out again, what am I going to do?" Joy and I finally decided that she should sit out on the patio, with a book to read, and just keep an eye on Aila from outside the house.

There was also an incident where Aila, I don't know how she managed to do it, remembered the 911 number and called the police. She told them that there was a group of my graduate students outside the house demanding I change their grades in one of the courses that they had just completed. According to Aila, there must have been at least fifteen students and they were making a great deal of noise. Of course the police came to investigate and Joy had to explain to them that there was no group of students, that there was no one complaining about their grade and that she hoped they would understand that Aila had Alzheimer's disease.

Another problem that frequently manifests itself during this period is that the person loses all understanding of time. They don't know the time of day. They don't know if it is breakfast, lunch or supper time. Quite often, Aila would look at me and say, "Arthur would you please get me a new clock I cannot tell the time on this one, there is something wrong with the numbers." There was nothing wrong with the numbers, Aila was losing the ability to read the clock. I had read in other books dealing with Alzheimer's patients, that it is advisable to put up a chalkboard, probably in the kitchen, for notes and information that would be useful. Telephone numbers, things that they might do during the day, what time the caregiver would be coming home, and any other type of information that might be reassuring to them would probably be appropriate. I tried putting a large bulletin-board up in the kitchen next to the telephone but unfortunately, in Aila's case, it was too late; she could not read anything I put on it.

It is not unusual, either, at this stage of the disease, for Alzheimer's patients to misidentify people. I can remember an occasion in the grocery store. Aila was down at the meat counter, pushing the cart, getting the meat for the next couple of days, when a friend came down the aisle, put her arms around her and said, "Hi, Aila. How are you?" Aila's immediate reaction was, "I don't know who you are. How dare you touch me!" said in a very hostile manner. Unfortunately, her friend was not aware at that time that Aila had Alzheimer's disease.

It is not unusual, also, for the Alzheimer's patient to hallucinate. I cannot tell you how many times, when we were sitting in the living room, Aila said, "Can we please get out of this hotel? This is a terrible lobby, there are too many people here." I would say to her, "What do you mean, there are too many people in this lobby?" and she would say, "Just look at all the people who are wondering around here and I don't know any of them." This was frightening for her as well as me.

It becomes very obvious at this time that the Alzheimer's patient needs some physical help doing everyday, routine things. Aila would often put on her clothes the wrong side out. If she happened to get one arm in her sweater incorrectly, she would have no idea how to take the sweater off or how to rearrange it so that she could put the other arm in and make the sweater fit.

It was at this stage of Alzheimer's disease that I was told that I should investigate institutions, nursing homes that would be appropriate for Alzheimer's patients. Frequently, this advice is given at the end of the second phase or the beginning of the third.

And so life progressed.

In summary, what can I say about the second stage of Alzheimer's disease? Patients become increasingly slow to understand the world around them. They will often search for words during a conversation and will need more time to process what they hear and what they say. The ability to both calculate and understand time deteriorates rapidly. There begins a removal of self from the feelings, concerns and problems of others, a withdrawal into self. Behaviourial changes are probably the most observable facet of the disease during this stage.

Stage Three
The third stage of Alzheimer's disease can be described as moderately severe to severe and approximates the level of development of a child from approximately one to three years

of age. Along with the disabilities and dysfunctions that continue from stages one and two, a number of new facets appear in stage three that leave no doubt that the individual is obviously disabled.

Behaviourial changes continue to occur: anger, increased confusion, detachment from the family and loved ones. It was at the end of the second stage and into the third that Aila began to see me as someone other than Arthur, her husband. She would often ask me who I was and why I was in the house. I was accepted as a friend. I was, at various times, her cousin, brother or father. Along with Joy I managed to feed, wash, clothe, love and keep her from harms way. It was indeed a twenty-four-hour day!

The caregiver, during this stage, no longer functions as a loving companion and helper, but takes on the role of a caretaker. The person known disappears day by day before your eyes. The dying of the light is experienced not only by the Alzheimer's patient but also by the caregiver. The caregiver's life narrows, focusing only on the loved one who needs care and protection.

Orientation to time and place become more confusing. Although we have lived in the same house for several years, Aila would have to ask directions to the bathroom and to the kitchen, or be taken by the hand to locate them. Sometimes the need to go to the toilet passed before the directions were asked. Incontinence may be a minor problem at this stage.

It was at the beginning of stage three that Aila went to the Oak Bay Kiwanis Pavilion for long-term care.

And so life progressed.

In summary, what can I say about the third stage of Alzheimer's disease? There are marked behaviourial changes as the patient experiences greater uncertainty in knowing how to act and in orienting herself to time and place. Misidentification of people is common. The person usually gives the

Table 1. Functional Assessment Stages – Normal Aging / Alzheimer's Disease

Stage of Normal Aging Alzheimer's Disease	Estimated Duration of stages in Normal Aging & Alzheimer's Disease	Approximate Age at Which Function is Acquired in Normal Development	Functional Assessment Stages	Diagnosis for Alzheimer's Disease
1	50 years	Normal adult	No decrement	Normal adult
2	15 years	Normal aged adult	Subjective deficit in word finding	Normal aged adult
3	7 years	Young adult	Deficit in demanding employment settings	Compatible with incipient Alzheimer's Disease
				Alzheimer's Disease
4	2 years	Age 8 to adolescence	Requires help in complex tasks e.g. handling finances or, planning dinner for guests	Mild
5	18 months	Age 5 to 7	Requires help choosing proper clothing to wear	Moderate
6a	5 months	Approx. 5 years	Requires help in dressing	Moderately severe
6b	5 months	Approx. 4 years	Requires help in bathing	Moderately severe
6c	5 months	Approx. 48 months	Requires help toileting (flushing, wiping, etc.)	Moderately severe
6d	4 months	Approx. 36-54 months	Urinary incontinence	Moderately severe
6e	12 months	Approx. 24-36 months	Fecal incontinence	Moderately severe
7a	12 months	Approx. 15 months	Can speak only approx. 5-6 intelligible words	Severe
7b	18 months	Approx. 12 months	Intelligible vocabulary limited to a single word	Severe
7c	12 months	Approx. 12 months	Cannot walk independently	Severe
7d	12 months	Approx. 6-10 months	Cannot sit up independently	Severe
7e	12 months	Approx. 8-16 weeks	Cannot smile	Severe
7f	Not applicable	Approx. 4-12 weeks	Cannot hold up head independently	Severe

Phase 1
Phase 3
Phase 3
Phase 4

Source: Reisberg, Barry. Dementia: A systematic approach to identifying reversible causes. **Geriatrics**, April 1986, Vol. 41, No. 4, pp. 30-45.
See Chapter 10 for complete details

impression of being lethargic and unconcerned about others. It is also not unusual for the patient to hallucinate.

Stage Four

The fourth and final stage of Alzheimer's disease can be described as severe and approximates the developmental level of an infant from four to fifteen months of age. Along with a composite of the dysfunctions characteristic of the first three stages, the individual becomes totally disabled and must rely upon the care of others for the most simple of tasks.

Speech becomes limited to a few words and there is usually a perseveration of phrases, words or syllables. The example in the poem in the introduction where Aila says, "happy, happy, happy," is an indication of this type of behaviour. The person loses all contact with the world around him and makes no eye contact with other people. It is indeed the last flicker of the light.

Aila, at this point in my writing (November 1990), is totally disabled. She is incontinent and cannot feed herself because of the tremor in her hands. Every day I see her at lunch and help to feed her. I would certainly recommend that a loved one visit an individual with Alzheimer's disease at a time when they can participate in the care of the patient. It provides an opportunity for a loved one to remain a part of the process. Aila is no longer able to communicate. She remains in a world of her own, thankfully a peaceful world. She cannot stand or walk. She is moved each day from her bed into her wheelchair or recliner by a hydraulic lift. Her back, from the waist up, is frozen into a rigid position, as are her legs, because the brain no longer can function to tell them how to bend or move. Each night I pray that she will, "go gentle into that good night."

And so life progresses.

In summary, what can I say about the fourth stage of Alzheimer's disease? It is the end, my friends. It enriches us in our understanding of man's humanity and it makes our souls cry.

Chapter 3

BREAKING THE NEWS

A diagnosis of Alzheimer's disease is not the end of life, but the beginning of a new phase of life. It requires the making of difficult decisions that will not wait for a later time and the assuming of responsibilities that were never anticipated. The victim of Alzheimer's disease is no less a person because he or she has the disease. Victims' rights and expectations are not diminished because of their disabilities. Alzheimer's sufferers feel pain. They react to love. They laugh. They cry. They smile, and they respond to tenderness. But how do you tell your loved ones that they have the disease and that they are going to die?

Telling Yourself

After the diagnosis has been confirmed, a decision has to be made by someone to tell the patient of his or her fate. Who will it be: doctor, husband/wife, daughter/son or friend?

The first person who has to understand the problems and events that will take place over the next several years is you, the primary caregiver. The first reaction is one of denial and confusion. There are also feelings of betrayal by the loved one and a sinking feeling that all your future hopes and plans are gone. Eventually, there comes a feeling of resignation. Your responsibilities include sickness as well as health. You said the words when you married, now is the time to deliver. You, as the caregiver, also have a responsibility to yourself and to others in the family. You are not alone and all family members should be expected to share in the caregiving to the extent of their ability and circumstances. However, this still places most of the burden upon the primary caregiver, and you must be realistic about your personal health and the economic resources available to you.

There are three stages that are critical in your ability to function as a caregiver. The first stage occurs when you, as the caregiver, feel comfortable in being able to handle the situation. The second stage arrives when you can no longer function as the caregiver without some period of rest away from your responsibilities. You cannot continue to function as an individual, in your own right, without some help in caring for the patient. Stage three arrives when, even with help and some periods of respite, you cannot deal with the twenty-four hours of constant care that is required. Your danger area of functioning arrives when you are spending more hours per day caring for the patient than for yourself.

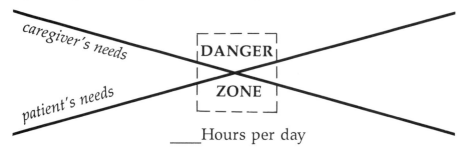

At this point in the progression of the disease, an alternative method of care needs to be considered.

I still haven't answered the question, however, as to how you tell yourself. In my situation, the point arrived when I had to actually say the words to another person, "Aila has Alzheimer's disease." It really doesn't become meaningful until you have said it, and then it is almost as if someone has given you a blow. The words seem strange to you, they seem unfamiliar and they certainly feel uncomfortable. I found myself going for weeks refusing to talk about Aila's illness because it was impossible to express myself without tears welling up. Gradually, I found, however, that the more I expressed my feelings and talked of the progress of the disease, the easier it was to become at peace with myself. Strangely enough, I find it easier to talk with friends than to family members. Family members want to know more than the superficial. They ask for the details, but for the caregiver, it is impossible to communicate the reality.

Rights of the Alzheimer's Patient

One of the rights of the Alzheimer's patient is the right to be supported. The patient has the right to receive the best health care that is available. It is unfair that the individual be denied the appropriate care necessary to lead as full and functional a life as is possible in each stage of development of the disease. It is also best to be sure that the victim and caregiver understand what resources are at their disposal to help understand the choices and options available. The patient should not be forced into day-care situations without an opportunity to view the facility and observe its activities. The individual may not be comfortable in the situation.

The individual also has the right to know about the disease. Exactly how to tell a patient is difficult to answer, for it depends upon the stage of development of the disease when a firm diagnosis is made. If an individual is in the early stages of the disease, I believe it is probably best for a specialist to tell the patient in a medical facility with the husband/wife/ daughter/son, whoever is the primary caregiver, there with the individual. In the case of Aila, this was not possible. We did not determine that Aila had Alzheimer's disease until she was at the stage where her short-term memory would not function from one-half hour to the next. She was also unable to comprehend the description of Alzheimer's disease and what it meant to her. I can remember the evening that I told her the doctor had called and confirmed that she had the disease. I was sitting on the couch next to her telling her that I had talked to the doctor and that he had confirmed what I had anticipated — she did indeed have Alzheimer's. I started to tell Aila and broke down crying. Aila, being the woman she is, put her arms around me and said, "Don't cry my dear it will be all right. We have handled other problems in our life and we can handle this one too." I found myself in the strange situation of being the one who wanted to comfort her when in reality she was comforting me. I have often thought of other situations since then and marvel at the woman I married. There is a line that I remember from the play *The Lion in Winter*, "What a great fool I would have been not to have loved you."

By not providing knowledge to the patients of what the disease entails, we are disempowering them. Without knowledge, they cannot make decisions, and there are times, during the development of Alzheimer's disease, when the patient is capable of making certain decisions. They may not be able to balance a bank-book, they may not remember what happened yesterday, but they may be able to fully comprehend what it means to make decisions concerning their assets when they are no longer with us, the disposition of their bodies when they die and the signing of legal documents such as power of attorney.

A third right of the individual is for the opportunity to grieve. Most Alzheimer's patients are very aware that something is wrong, that their abilities are diminishing, declining, falling away. Alzheimer's patients need to be given the opportunity to grieve with their families and loved ones. They need to understand fully that they have support, that they have loving care, and that everything will be done for them that is in their best interests. Not only do the patient and the primary caregiver need to be given this privilege of grieving, so too does the family.

It is the right of patients to plan for the disposition of their assets. Not only is Alzheimer's disease a very debilitating and devastating disease for the patient personally, but it is also, for the family, emotionally and, in many cases, financially devastating. At some point in the disease, most patients will be in need of long-term-care facilities. If some measures are not taken, before this time arrives, to protect what assets the family has, then the primary caregiver may find savings from a lifetime wiped out in a short period of time. It is imperative, therefore, that such a situation be prevented. Once the diagnosis is made, legal advice and support must be sought. It is important that assets be shielded whenever possible from the prohibitive costs of providing care.

Evaluating options for future health care certainly needs to be considered. The time will arrive in the progress of the disease when patients will have to go to long-term-care facilities. Before this time in the disease arrives, and while patients are still capable of providing input, those alternatives available should certainly be presented to them so that their wishes and desires can be carried out.

It would be wise for people in their early to mid-sixties to have wills in order that their wishes for burial arrangements are specified. They should also be aware of legal options which are available to ensure that the economic well-being of any survivor is not placed in jeopardy.

Within the last few years, the idea of living wills has become particularly prevalent in discussions with terminally ill patients. You need to check your local laws to determine the extent of the power of a living will. Often, the living will has no legal authority but is merely an indicator of your preferences. It allows an individual to express his or her wishes regarding both the extension of life through support systems and preferences regarding terminal care.

Telling the Family

The family structure has changed over the years with the development of the industrialized society. No longer do extended family units live in close proximity to one another and certainly the social unit of several generations in one home is almost extinct. Today, families come in all shapes and sizes. Some cultural groups have in their philosophical foundations the concept of care for the older members of the family that is part of their heritage. For other members of society, the care by the children of their parents may not be a fundamental concept. The psychological and social make-up of each family is unique and often confuses the issue of who becomes the primary caregiver and how the family functions.

When telling the family that a loved one has Alzheimer's disease, we need to consider two questions: Who is the caregiver?

and What is the relationship of the caregiver(s) to the patient? It is important, for example, to know if the primary caregiver is in the relationship as husband or wife. Spouses are usually more dedicated to the care of patients than are their children. It may be easier for the children, therefore, to consider long-term-care facilities than it is for the spouse. Wives frequently seem to have more difficulty in being caregivers than do husbands. This is probably because of cultural and social expectations as well as economic burdens placed upon them. It is not unusual to have pension plans that expire upon the death of the worker. Since more men than women have pension plans, and savings may be quickly used, the survivor (wife) could be left without any continuing funding.

The opportunity for conflict over the care of the Alzheimer's patient can increase unless the family is aware of the needs of the patient as the disease develops and has established some guidelines for decision-making and responsibility. If, for example, the patient, either male or female, was in all respects the head of the family and made most of the decisions for the well-being of the family, or was the emotional rock of the family to whom everyone turned for advice and support , the patient's illness would be devastating. The family is likely to have trouble in organizing support and may argue about the degree of support and involvement expected from each member. The result may be that, because of a lack of leadership, both the patient and primary caregiver become secondary issues and focus is lost. Minority cultures within the community are often faced with this type of problem because of the differing roles of the male/female within family structures.

If the primary caregiver is the central figure in the family, the family will likely function as a strong support group. Members of the family will usually support the decisions of the caregiver and will look to that person to keep the communication channels open. It must be realized, however, that this places an added burden upon the caregiver. The caregiver not only has to act as a support for the patient but must now function as the sole family communicator and the decision maker for the patient — not an enviable position. A lack of this type of decision making may impair the individual's ability to function in the role of primary caregiver.

Telling Friends

Friends may or may not be aware of the development of the disease in their friend who has Alzheimer's disease. If they are knowledgeable, the process of helping them to understand the behaviour of the patient is so much easier. They are aware that the verbal and non-verbal responses they observe, so unlike the person they know, are caused by the disease.

I have found that friends form a valuable support group in the beginning but as time passes the pressure on the friends is confounded by several extremely human traits. The first is the change in the relationship with an old friend who has Alzheimer's disease. Current events cannot be discussed, the repetition of the same stories and questions becomes old hat until eventually the patient becomes an irritant in social inter-action and so contact decreases.

A second factor is what might be referred to as the mirror-image complex — the understanding that as we get older our chances of getting Alzheimer's disease increase. The thought is not very comforting and to be frequently in the company of someone whom you know is going to die hits close to our own mortality.

A third factor deals with the social structure of the relationship between couples. As the relationships change because of the behaviour of the Alzheimer's patient, the interaction and social make-up of the group changes. The resultant pressures are un-derstandable. The caregiver needs to understand the factors affecting long-time relationships and should seek support from additional sources such as the Alzheimer's Disease Support Group.

A normal tendency of the caregiver, in dealing with occasional friends and acquaintances is to avoid them. You get tired of explaining behaviour or the effects of the disease on behaviour and you do not want to be constantly put in the position of having to apologize. This is normal behaviour on the part of the caregiver, but it only adds to his or her own isolation. A better solution would be to attend group gatherings without the Alzheimer's patient. This may be difficult but it is imperative for your own survival as a caregiver. One man I know whose wife had Alzheimer's disease, had cards printed that he would hand to acquaintances or store personnel when the patient's behaviour had the potential of causing a problem. The card read:

My wife has Alzheimer's disease. Please be patient with us.
Thank you for your kindness.

Chapter 4

CARE AND FEEDING OF THE CAREGIVER

This chapter's title is not meant to be humorous. I chose it to express the tender, loving care that is needed for the caregiver. The caregiver to an Alzheimer's patient is also a victim of the disease. He or she frequently suffers depression that does not cease after the death of the loved one. That depression can become a permanent emotional state which may become as debilitating as the Alzheimer's disease itself.

The reasons for depression are not difficult to fathom. Spouses live in social limbo where they must once again function as a single people after years of married life. They lack partners for social activities that are usually organized for couples, but are not free to engage in activities that would help them acquire partners. They cannot mourn their loss because their husbands/wives are still living, nor can they divorce their afflicted spouses; society would segregate them even further from the social interaction they need should they abandon lifelong partners.

Just as all patients will not react in the same way to Alzheimer's disease, nor will all caregivers. Some will regard the repetition of questions by the patient as a deliberate way to annoy them. Behaviours that might have once been minor irritations, not worthy of attention and comment, become major irritants that cause frustration, anxiety and sometimes even anger. The resultant reaction on the part of the caregiver leads to feelings of guilt that are often compounded as the ability to deal with the frustration diminishes. Even when the patient is institutionalized, the caregiver may not experience a sense of release, even though some of the burden of care has been shifted.

Home and Community Resources

The best type of care for the Alzheimer's patient usually takes place in the home where the person is under the supervision and control of the family. Wives, husbands, sons, daughters and close relatives are generally the people who are closest to the patient and it is they who are responsible for the major care that is given. Spouses are most often bonded by years of love and are probably correct in thinking that they can provide the best care that is possible.

Most families keep their Alzheimer's relatives at home for a period of time until it becomes absolutely necessary that they become institutionalized. One of the reasons for this is love for the patient. Another is the extremely high financial and emotional cost to the family in placing a patient in an institution where they believe the quality of life would not be as great as it would be at home.

As the disease progresses, it becomes obvious that the job of taking care of the patient is intensive and is indeed a thirty-six-hour day. The spouse is likely to be the primary caregiver and because of the need of constant vigilance may be unable to sleep at night, to run errands, or feel that he or she can have any life independent from the patient. Depending upon the ages of the caregiver and the patient, it is not unusual for a career to be ended in order for the caregiver to stay at home with the patient. As age increases in both the caregiver and the patient, the caregiver may also experience poor physical health and the patient then poses an additional burden to the overall well-being of the caregiver.

There are several support systems available in the community. The network of community-based services is extensive in most locales and a service plan can usually be tailor-made to aid both the patient and the spouse. Counselling is also available for the caregiver and in many cases this is a great help. The types of services that one might find are:

- home health care,
- adult-care services (often these are specialized for the Alzheimer's patient),
- visiting-nurse care,
- in some cases occupational and physical therapy,
- home meal delivery programs,
- transportation,
- information and referral services,
- home makers that will often do chores around the home that neither the caregiver nor patient are capable of performing,
- respite care that may be available in some local institutions for short periods of time,
- mental-health services,
- legal services,
- companionship programs, and housing assistance.

In communities where there is no formal network available, families may be able to form their own network, among families with similar problems, through their local churches, nursing homes and hospitals.

The services that seem to be of most value for the Alzheimer's patient living at home are generally the in-home service and respite care. Families find that they desperately need in-home services. These services are often activities which keep Alzheimer's patients occupied: talking with them, playing games with them, taking them for rides or taking them for walks. Any number of things that would aid in the physical exercise of patients as well as providing them with meaningful activities are useful. The in-home service person may also provide housekeeping services that would be necessary if the primary caregiver was working away from home every day. A wide range of these in-home services is available, some of them include therapy, nursing care, home health aid and home makers who provide housekeeping services.

Another category of invaluable care for an Alzheimer's caregiver is the respite care. Respite care is defined in a variety of ways but it generally means substitute care for a short duration of time, usually a number of hours, sometimes a day, or in some cases even a period of two or three weeks, when the relief is of primary necessity for the caregiver. My experience with respite care, however, is that it is usually available on a private-room basis in an institution that provides care for Alzheimer's patients only. Because Alzheimer's patients are only there for a short period of time and not on a long-term-care basis, little attempt is made to get the patients involved in the activities of the institution. Frequently one finds the Alzheimer's patient sitting in his or her room and doing absolutely nothing. In my experience, the guilt of not having Aila stimulated and involved in activities for a two-week period while I had some respite overrode any beneficial effects of the rest period. I found myself going to the institution every day and talking to her and taking her for walks or a ride. After ten days of what was supposed to be a month's respite, I took her home because I couldn't justify keeping her there any longer. I was lonesome, I missed her and I knew that she needed me.

It is also possible that a caregiver may be able to find day-care services that will provide, for one or more days or perhaps even a week, care in the home twenty-four hours a day. This kind of service, with a competent caregiver, is very difficult to find and is quite expensive. There is a possibility that other short-term arrangements can be made such as boarding. In some cases situations work out well and are life-savers for the caregiver. In other situations, all they do is compound the existing burden and frustration.

In the United States, it is possible to find agencies which may be of help through both area agencies on ageing and some local health departments. In Canada it is best to go to the provincial ministry offices of Health and Human Resources to obtain guidelines and information on services which may be available. If the patient, family or caregiver is in need of help, these agencies can provide appropriate services and additional information which may be needed.

Other agencies which might be considered are nursing programs in community colleges or universities providing they are close enough. They can often provide information on services which are available in the locale. Also one should not forget one's family physician. Particularly in the case of Alzheimer's disease, there are brochures available which physicians may have for distribution in their offices. Local hospitals and patient- referral offices may often have information available on local Alzheimer's organizations, where they can be found, and what literature is available. All of these services are available to the Alzheimer's patient caregiver and should be investigated thoroughly.

Strategies for Relieving Stress

It is imperative that caregivers who are looking after Alzheimer's patients be well informed as to what the disease is, how it manifests itself and how we as caregivers can best deal with it without causing ourselves undue stress. This is the primary reason I am writing this book. When I started to look for information, I found some but not all that I needed. I thought that someday when I could talk about Aila and her disease, it would be useful to put down information which I, myself, would have liked to know.

There are strategies that can be used to deal with Alzheimer's patients' behaviour that can help alleviate stress.

1. Alzheimer's patients are not trying to make us angry by repeating questions. They do not know that they are repeating questions. This is important in our understanding. We must accept this. Every time (even though it may be the tenth) he repeats the question, it is a new question for him. He has not asked it before (in his mind) and if we respond in any other way than how we would if the question were asked for the first time, we will create stress in ourselves and the patient will become upset and wonder what he has done wrong and why we are responding in such a fashion.

2. It is very difficult to correct an Alzheimer's patient when he or she has done something wrong. Patients don't know that what they have done is wrong. She may have put her sweater on inside out or only have one arm in her sweater and cannot find a way of getting the other arm in. Sometimes she won't know how to take the sweater off and start all over again. This requires patience; the Alzheimer's patient is not doing it to make you angry, she is doing it because she doesn't know how to do it differently. We must see the disease for what it is. It is a lessening of one's power to think. It is a lessening of one's power to observe. It is a lessening of one's power to function. This is very stressful to the caregiver but once you realize what it is, it is easier to deal with the stress. While observing the health-care staff at the Oak Bay Kiwanis Pavilion, I am often amazed at the kindness and gentleness extended by them to the caregiver experiencing stress. They know what the disease is and how to handle it. True, they do not have the same emotional involvement, but if we are to help the Alzheimer's patient at home, we must try to respond in the same way as staff workers in an institution, that is with kindness, consideration and an awareness of why patients behave the way they do.

3. Often times, too much is asked of Alzheimer's patients. For example, don't ask, "Will you go to the kitchen and bring me the newspaper?" That is too difficult for many patients as the disease progresses. They can go out to the kitchen, but by the time they get out there they have forgotten why they are there. Sometimes when you say "the kitchen," they get half way there and then cannot remember where they are going. We may get angry, particularly if we are not aware that we are dealing

with an Alzheimer's patient, but if we have information, if we have understanding, we can deal with the stress. I have also found that, in working with Aila, positive reinforcement is extremely important. You cannot get angry. It only makes your blood pressure rise and it doesn't help the patient. It only adds confusion and frustration, and the reaction from the patient is, "Why are you mad at me, why are you doing this to me?" The reinforcement that we give has to be positive. I find that even now, as Aila is getting towards the end of the disease, I am still able to tell whether she is making a statement or asking a question. If I understand that I am to respond by providing information to her, I do, even though I know she doesn't understand or the topic may be unrelated to her thoughts. I talk to her as if I am giving her information and carrying on a normal conversation. It is not unusual for us to talk for four or five minutes without either one of us having any understanding of what we are saying. I don't know what she is asking me to respond to but she seems to be happy at the way I am responding.

That's what I mean by positive reinforcement. We have to observe, react and feed back to them in a manner that seems to communicate with them. If Aila asks a question and I respond, "Yes, sure, everything is alright." She will look at me and say, "Yeah" and smile and sit back for a minute and then go on with something else. It is not difficult for us to do and it is certainly not too much for loved ones to ask of us.

Support Groups

Alzheimer's support groups are usually available in most communities of reasonable size. You may be interested in a support group. Talking with people who experience the same problems and who can provide understanding for your problems may help you to understand what resources are available. They may be able to give you hints in coping with the Alzheimer's patient. You should consider joining such a group. Such groups usually meet once a month, generally in the same location, usually a hospital, health facility or a municipal building. The one thing that you should consider, when making a decision as to whether you wish to make use of such a group, however, is the qualifications and training of the group leader. It is extremely important that the leader of the group have a thorough understanding of the problems of the disease and have skills and the ability to work with people. It is also worthwhile noting here that not all people benefit from this kind of group interaction. Research indicates that about one-third of people who seek help from an Alzheimer's group find that the meeting with the group does nothing but increase their anxiety level. If you find this yourself, for Heaven's sake, don't feel guilty about giving up the group. Some of us aren't groupies. Some of us don't like to express our feelings in public. It doesn't mean that we are abnormal and that we aren't communicative. It merely means that we have discovered other ways of handling our stress and problems that are satisfactory for us. Group situations are not for everyone. You should explore them to see if they are helpful to you but if they are not of value you should not feel guilty.

Institutional Caregivers — A Dialogue

The Alzheimer's Ward

Arthur Olson

They walk, sit unaware,
An endless state of being — uninvolved.

The hours pass, not alone,
In conversation with images we cannot see.
They nod, sometimes they smile and talk
in sounds we do not know.
Some rage from past, now visible images — unwanted.

Some carry dolls and think of them as real.
They were good girls.
They were good girls.
I like them.
I like them.

Bob walks the corridor — searching,
He grabs a hand, holds tight as if to touch something
real to help him back.
Some sit or lie in wait,
Anticipating a gentle touch to caress their lips and be as one.

Caregivers are not just limited to the home. Once an Alzheimer's disease patient is institutionalized, a new, significant caregiver becomes important — the health-care worker. These new friends of the patient become responsible for day-to-day physical care and grooming.

The following is a discussion I had with Maria, a health-care worker (caregiver), who depicts the humanity, gentleness and kindness of the people who take over from us our role as caregiver.

"When a resident comes into the facility, we try to make them comfortable right away. We introduce ourselves and offer them a cup of tea. Then their belongings are moved into their room. It can either be traumatic or not traumatic. When I first saw Aila, when you were walking down the hall, the thing that struck me about Aila was her stature. I enjoyed taking her for walks and talking with her. She was really an enlightenment to me. We never had a problem of affinity. We both came from Europe and like to travel. She talked about her line of work and that set the ground work for my getting involved. Several times when Aila was having a difficult day, the nurse would ask me to see what I could do to calm her and make things easier. If I was not able to do it, there would be someone else that could be with her in her space. After a period of time, it would start to work on me. I felt very frustrated at times because I was not able to do more but just practice patience.

"After I read the first three chapters of your book, I thought to myself, How can I possibly say anything more than what I had already read. Our part (the health-care worker) was just starting. What could I do except show my concern, just show my love to her — that I cared, that we all cared. I loved going for walks with her and watching her enjoyment."

What about the specific concerns that residents generally have when they come in?

"The patients are confused and they don't understand what this 'hotel' is all about. We reassure them that we are here to help them and look after them. Sometimes we are able to make them understand that they are here so that the people who have been taking care of them can take a break. They want to know 'But will I go back?' No, this is your home. This is something that Aila didn't understand. 'Why can't I go home?' Although she did go home on visits her attention span wasn't long enough for her to remember.

"One day I was feeding one of the residents and I let Aila come with me. She said to me, 'Why doesn't he talk?' I told her that he was sick. She grabbed his hand and said, 'Hello, I'm Aila Olson, and I have Alzheimer's and I am going to get better. If I get better you will get better too.' That really grabbed me. I often thought, Wouldn't it be wonderful to go in and out and be able to stay out when we wanted. That would be a fantastic choice, one that Alzheimer's residents do not have."

How do people react when they come in?

"Some like Aila, are questioning — looking around, trying to figure things out. Others you can see in their eyes that they don't understand what this is, who those people are, why they have to do what we say. Some become frightened and regress back into their own shells. Others in earlier stages of the disease than Aila showed disbelief, frustration, 'I don't belong here, What am I going to do?'"

Does the disease usually progress more rapidly after they get in?

"Yes, unfortunately. There have been many studies done with different patients. Does one's defense mechanism kick in or do we adhere to the atmosphere around. At times you can visibly see them struggle to cope with the residents around them who have the same but more advanced Alzheimer's disease. I don't know if other facilities experience the same thing. It comes up in discussion and we express how much it hurts us to see this process taking place."

Do you find that they regress back to much earlier experiences, for example, Aila went back to her early teens in Finland?

"When I spoke with her she was always on her job or on holidays. On her job she would have been older. I detected a lot of dislike toward some of the people with whom she dealt. I didn't want to get into that sort of thing because you just aggravate the situation but if she spoke about her time on the farm or picnicking you picked up on that and tried to work with that because those were happy times."

What is the reaction to you as the new caregiver?

"We cannot replace you because there is a bond. As long as they remember what the bond is they will hang on to it. We on the other hand are friends, we cannot replace a wife, husband, sister or brother — who looks after them. Sometimes they allow you to work with them and sometimes they don't. Whatever they say to you, you cannot take personally because it is the disease that is talking."

How do the primary caretakers respond to the staff?

"We have to understand that this is someone that you love and what you see you have no control over. Normally people like to feel that they can control to a certain degree. I don't know what kind of a day you have had at home or at work. You may come in and see something that you want changed and you approach us in a grouchy tone of voice. We try to practice diplomacy and take your approach in stride because we realize that you are dealing with something that is really 'heavy.' We can't begin to build an attitude towards you — you are as important as the resident."

What would you like to see a visitor do?

"I would like to see them be able to relax with the resident and not show frustration or apprehension. I know residents pick up on that. They are very sensitive. If there happens to be a mishap with someone having fallen, they become caring and alert. They also pick up on other residents' outbursts. We have to remain cool so to speak."

Is there a special time of day to come to visit? For example, my feeling is that the best time for me to come is to give her lunch, because it gives us something to do. Is there any other time that would be useful? When she could get in the car, we always went down to the beach but she can't do that any more.

"I think that when the weather improves it would be nice for Aila and many others to go out to feel the fresh air. It is always a challenge."

What is the feeling about different members of the family coming in?

"It's funny that you mention that. Throughout the whole manuscript that I have read so far, you touched upon friends, and I thought, You know, I never saw anybody, except the first year Aila saw the children and other members of the family. It made me think about the time my father had cancer. How friends just disappeared. They can't handle it. How many of Aila's friends could come in now and see her like that?"

What about younger children coming to visit?

"The patients love children. Have you ever been downstairs when they have kiddies' day? It is cute. The patients respond — something sparks in them. It is explained to the children that they should not be afraid of the residents — that the residents are not well. The children accept that so readily — it's beautiful to see them in their company."

When I brought our oldest grandchild in last summer, Aila didn't even know that he was in the room.

"Sometimes residents respond when someone enters the room and other times you need to have direct eye contact with them. It happens quite often with me. I walk into the room and Aila isn't talking or anything. We make contact and instantly you can see her facial expression change. Maybe your grandchild wasn't prepared to see her the way she was — maybe he expected something more."

What I notice too is the humour on the unit. I don't think you could survive or cope without it. Do you do it consciously to try to create a congenial atmosphere, not only for yourselves but for the patients as well?

"Most of the time when you talk to staff around 1:00 pm (we have been up since 5:30 am) you notice that the day is starting to wear on us. Then humour will start to come into play. It is a very necessary requirement.

"In the morning, one comes off of the elevator and soon there is a feeling of becoming like a chameleon. Each resident has a different level that they are functioning at, and we the staff are like the equalizers on a stereo set, adjusting to all the mood levels. This is where humour is important. Laughing is infectious — the domino effect starts. It doesn't happen all the time, but when it does, it's a pleasure to be part of it or to be the instigator of it. It is definitely a stress releaser for us.

"Music also plays a big part in daily happenings. At one time, not too long ago, a few of our residents loved to listen to music and were very good dancers. At 9 am, or after breakfast, we were dancing polkas and waltzes with them in the lounges. It was a beautiful thing to see and feel. 'Each time we listen to beautiful music, we select an impression to weave into the harmony of our unfoldment' (F.A. Newhouse). And so the thought runs through my mind, God loves you and so do I."

Financial and Legal Questions

There are numerous questions for which we need information when our loved one becomes ill. The following are some questions with answers that are frequently asked by caregivers.

It is not my purpose to discuss with you in detail the legal and financial issues that should be considered when faced with

Alzheimer's disease but rather, to give you the benefits of my experience and the advice I received.

1. Should I have a will?

Yes, you should. Without a will your wishes will not be considered when you die. The courts will decide on the disposition of all your property and the chances for family conflict are increased.

2. Should I sign a power of attorney?

A power of attorney is a legal document by which you grant to someone the authority to act on your behalf in all or specific matters. In the case of an Alzheimer's patient, a husband, wife or close relative may be entrusted with the management of your affairs. If you have any concerns about the date on which the trustee signs the document to become your legal representative, you may wish to have your lawyer, in conjunction with your doctor(s), make the decision as to when the power of attorney comes into effect. This will ensure that you stay in control of your affairs for as long as possible.

The answer is, once again, yes. The decision to sign a power of attorney *must* be made while the person is still able to manage his own affairs and can comprehend the intent and meaning of the power of attorney.

It is inevitable that in the process of the disease, a point will be reached when the person will no longer be able to make rational decisions concerning his economic affairs or the state of his well-being. If a power of attorney is not in place with the courts when this point in the process of the disease is reached, then the family must go to the courts to have a trustee appointed. This places an added burden on the family both psychologically and financially.

The process may seem straight forward and uncomplicated, but in reality, it may not progress as planned. When I felt a power of attorney was needed for Aila, she was at the point in the disease where she understood its significance but was anxious and suspicious of many things. To relieve her anxiety we talked about a power of attorney and we both signed the power-of-attorney paper at the same time. She seemed to feel better, understanding that we were both doing the same thing.

As with the will, the power of attorney should be kept in a safe place. I would suggest that the attorney you selected keep the originals in the safe of his firm's office and that you retain a copy. You should inform the trustee of both of these documents with the name of the law firm and the location of both the originals and copies.

3. What is a trustee and should I have one?

A trustee is a person responsible for the property or affairs of another person. In the event that you have signed a will and you have died, you probably have designated a trustee to settle your financial affairs. In the case where no trustee has been designated by you, the court will assign a trustee.

4. Should I have a joint checking and/or savings account with a person afflicted with Alzheimer's disease?

No! As the disease progresses it is not unusual to find a period of time in which the person's normal judgement and common sense have been considerably lessened. He may become suspicious and secretive in his behaviour.

Aila, during the early stages, was very susceptible to anyone who came to the door selling merchandise. Several religious groups also found her a willing donator of cash and made weekly visits. Later, Aila felt that the money was not safe in the bank and wanted to put it in her pocket book under our bed.

I went to our bank and explained Aila's condition to them. Legally there was no way that they could prevent her from removing funds from the accounts that had both of our signatures. For a long time, I tried to divert her attention and hide the cheque-book. The time did come when I had to remove her name from our account. Aila felt comfortable with an old cheque-book in her possession, and since she had lost the ability to read or write, the whole question eventually became academic.

Soul

Content in an empty room
I look and see it all,
Remembering the joy, the laughter and the tears -
    the empty vase upon a table.
I wonder what it means?

I passed the room each day.
The rose red decanter on the table by the window.
Half full, I think.
Two glasses waiting for a visitor.

The image never changed.
Year after year the wine remained the same.
The glasses dulling in the sun...
Waiting.

And then one day the glasses were gone.
The window dulled in the sunlight -
    its gray reflection filtering the winter sun.
The vase no longer bright.
A sediment covered the once bright
    reflection from the table.

The images - ghosts.
Laughter, joy and sorrow dulled,
I sit content in this empty room...

Chapter 5

HOME-SAFETY TIPS

For the public in general, accidents happen more frequently in the home than anywhere else. For the Alzheimer's patient the chances of having an accident in the home are great. There are several problems that exist. One is that the person may try to do things that he or she previously could do but is no longer able to .This may involve a simple thing such as peeling a potato. The ability to do manual tasks is often forgotten by the Alzheimer's patient and can lead to accidents. One of the things that we must remember about Alzheimer's disease is that it is a process of unlearning, not a process of learning. It is very difficult and often impossible for patients to learn new tasks, but they do unlearn those tasks which they previously could carry out with a great deal of confidence. Because the person seems to be able to manage well, we assume that he can do the things which are normal activities around the household. As caregivers, we need to take precautions to make sure that accidents do not occur.

If the Alzheimer's patient seems to be caught in a series of accidents such as bumping into a table or dropping a cup of coffee or breaking a dish (all of which are unintentional) this is often an indication to you that the Alzheimer's patient is getting upset and needs to have his direction and activities changed so that a new approach can be taken. This is probably the time when a change of pace is necessary, a quiet time is necessary, sitting down is necessary or listening to music may be an advisable activity to avoid serious accidents.

It is important for the primary caregiver to be aware of the patient's impaired capabilities. If, for example, we know that they are no longer aware of whether they are turning on the hot or cold water faucets, are confused and are no longer able to read the letters C and H on the knobs, it is imperative that we accompany them to activities that involve turning on water faucets. This is particularly important in taking a bath. We do not want our loved ones to receive scalding burns.

It is also important that once a person has been diagnosed as having Alzheimer's, we look at our home to observe what we can do to make it safer. What are some of the things that we know can cause problems — in the neighbourhood, in the yard, in the upstairs bedroom, downstairs living room — that may have caused minor problems in the past but are likely to cause major problems in the future?

The Home

If the home has a great deal of furniture, a great many knick-knacks, and involves a great deal of manoeuvring to get from one room to the other, it needs to be looked at as a hazard for the Alzheimer's patient. Try to secure the things that could cause safety problems such as the electric frying-pan, the iron or the stove. Certainly do not allow the Alzheimer's patient near anything that is electrical in nature (such as a toaster, lawnmower, electric knife or sewing machine) as there is a great possibility that these appliances can no longer be operated safely. To make sure, these appliances should be stored in a place in the home where they are not easily accessible to the patient, or better yet, in a closet that can be locked.

One of the greatest hazards that an Alzheimer's patient faces is stairs. There are several reasons for this, one is that the patient may be starting to loose his or her balance, another is that his or her peripheral vision may not permit objects on the stairs to be seen. One of the things that I found very useful with Aila was to place a baby gate on the bottom of the stairs in the morning and at the top of the stairs at night. On several occasions this minimized the dangers of Aila wandering, at night particularly, and of her falling downstairs. Clutter on the stairs should always be avoided. It is possible to have books or even a chest on the stairs, particularly if they are on two levels. Such things can be hazardous because patients can bump into them on their way down, and if they do fall, the sharp edges on the furniture may cause a serious accident.

If you are concerned about the person turning on the hot water rather than the cold and possibly scalding themselves, have the thermostat of the water tank set to a lower temperature. It is also possible to affix a colour code to the hot-water faucet — a red knob to indicate hot. However, you should make sure that the Alzheimer's patient does in fact recognize red as meaning hot.

Often, furniture has sharp corners and may therefore cause problems. It is best, with an Alzheimer's patient in the house, to place the furniture away from the centre of the room so that there are few, if any, obstructions in the middle of the floor. Of course, it is necessary to remove china cabinets and glass coffee tables which may break and cause serious injury. Certainly, for those who have antiques in the home, while the Alzheimer's patient is still living there, it is best to remove them.

Probably the best advice to be given to the caregiver of an Alzheimer's patient is that the home should be made childproof. That generally means that medicine cabinets should be locked, sharp objects should be taken out of the way, and chemicals should be removed from under the sink (or wherever else they may be stored) and locked up.

The Outdoors

The outdoors presents many hazards that can also cause serious harm. Because the Alzheimer's patient may be experiencing problems with balance and difficulties with perceptual orientation, glass patio doors should be marked with decals or other recognizable visual signals to warn the patient that the door is indeed there. In talking with other caregivers, I have been made aware of a precaution that could prevent a serious accident. If you have light flooring in front of a glass door that may cause a problem, place a dark mat on the floor. The Alzheimer's patient may perceive this as a black hole and will not step on it and thus stay away from the door. It may not always work but it is worth a try.

Once outside, if there is a porch or deck, be sure that the railings and banisters are secure and that the steps have non-skid mats. If at all possible, the steps should be painted in contrasting colours.

The back yard has many traps waiting for a victim. The ground may be uneven, thorny bushes can cause scratches that lead to infection, and the clothes-line can cause neck injury.

The outside furniture must be sturdy and stable while wooden chairs and tables should be free of sharp corners and splinters. If the yard can be made secure with a fence, this is an added bonus.

Swimming pools are more readily available to families now than in the past and present a unique hazard. They should be fenced and locked so that no unsupervised person can use them. An Alzheimer's patient may have been an excellent swimmer before the onset of the disease but as the disease progresses, the person may loose the ability to swim and can become confused, frightened and disoriented. Remember that Alzheimer's disease results in an unlearning process where existing abilities are gradually lost.

Operating a Car

In the early stages of the disease it has been reported that a number of people are still able to drive. As the disease progresses, however, they frequently become lost or confused. The action they take to correct problems can be dangerous for other drivers because they cannot anticipate the results of their actions. They may make U-turns or drive down one-way streets. In their confusion, they may even go through red lights or stop signs.

The Alzheimer's patient should never be left alone in the car and certainly not left with the key in the ignition. Too many accidents have been caused by the handbrake being released, the ignition turned on or the automatic windows being closed on an arm or hand.

The patient cannot be left alone for very long. As the disease progressed in Aila, I found that even if I just went into the store for milk, she would get out of the car because she didn't know whose car it was or how she got there. I was her anchor, her reference point.

Additional Considerations

The following are some hints, from the U.S. Consumer Product Safety Commission, that need to be considered in making the home safe for the Alzheimer's disease patient:

Clothing

Buying:

Buy flame-resistant fabrics and clothing when possible. Tightly woven, heavy fabrics usually burn more slowly than sheer, loosely woven ones; high-nap materials are likely to burn faster than smooth ones.

Washing:

Flame-resistant fabrics may require special washing, depending on the material and on the chemical treatment. Follow the instructions on the garment label.

Extra Precautions:

Store inflammable liquids in a well-ventilated area, away from any flame source, and out of sight and reach. Fuels such as gasoline should be stored away from your living quarters.

Closely supervise patients around space heaters, hot irons, stoves, lighted cigarettes and matches.

Poisons

Buying:

Avoid buying more of a hazardous substance than you are going to use right away. Read the warning labels. If you have a choice, buy products that have safety caps.

Using:

Keep the patient out of the area when using hazardous products and don't use the products around food or in places where children will play. Fumes and residues can linger in the atmosphere and on objects. If you are called away from the work area, take the product with you or place it tightly capped out of reach.

Storing:

Keep medicines in a cabinet that is out of reach. Lock it, if possible. Store other substances, such as cleaners, separate from medicines. If you carry medicine in your purse or coat pocket, keep an eye on it while patients are around or place it out of reach.

Leave hazardous products in their original containers. Don't store them under the kitchen sink or behind the toilet.

Disposing:

Leftover products of a hazardous nature should be discarded promptly and properly. Any that are placed in the trash should be buried well under other items. Medicine that is no longer needed can be returned to the druggist for appropriate disposal.

Stairs

The greatest single cause of home injuries is falls. Every year, 250,000 disabling injuries occur when people fall on stairs. Here are the most important factors in making stairways safe:

All steps should be the same measure.

Provide good lighting with switches at both the top and bottom of stairs.

Paint the edge of each step white, or paint a white patch on the floor above the highest and below the lowest step.

Avoid single steps, they are usually unexpected. Where a small change in level is unavoidable, install a ramp.

Install a handrail on each side of staircases. These should be forty-five to eighty-five centimetres above the treads and five to eight centimetres away from the wall to allow for a good grip.

The stair surface should never be slippery. Use rubber mats or carpeting. Mixing paint with sand is a simple way to put a non-slip surface on basement or outdoor steps.

If you use a stair carpet be sure it fits the contour of the stair snugly and is securely fastened. Inspect it frequently for worn spots and loose fastenings which could trip people.

Don't use throw rugs at the top or bottom of stairs.

Keep steps clear at all times. Don't use stairways as temporary storage areas.

Floors

To lessen the chance of falling, follow these rules:

If you have small throw rugs, be sure they can't easily slip on the floor. Use a non-slip rug pad. Skid-proof the back of the rug with spray or adhesive strips, available in rug and department stores. (Sprays wear off and have to be re-applied periodically.) Alternatively, tack the rug in place.

Keep floors and floor coverings in good condition. Check for tears and holes in rugs or linoleum and for loose tiles.

Clean up spills immediately. Be especially careful to thoroughly clean oil and grease spills.

When you wax your floors, choose a non-skid-type wax. Use it sparingly, following the manufacturer's instructions. Warn others of newly waxed floors.

Arrange the furniture so that there are unobstructed traffic ways through the rooms.

Do not string extension cords or other wires across walkways.

Provide mats at front and back doors for wiping off snow, mud, rain and other slippery materials that could be tracked in from outside.

Install night lights in rooms, in halls, bathrooms and stair areas.

Doors and Windows

Doors should swing into rooms, not into a flight of stairs or into a line of traffic.

All doors, including closet doors, should have handles for opening on both sides. Bedroom or bathroom doors which lock from the inside should have keys for unlocking from the outside.

Keep screens, guards and storm windows in good repair and firmly fastened.

If you have glass doors, here are some things you can do that will reduce the risk of injury:

Instead of ordinary glass, install plastic or safety glass.

Make the glass doors more visible: apply decals or coloured tape at adults' eye level.

Install safety bars on sliding glass doors. They show clearly when the door is closed and also tend to prevent contact with the glass. Install protective screens or grilles over the glass in storm doors.

Put furniture or planter boxes in front of the glass, so that it's not possible to run straight into it. Keep scatter rugs, toys and other small articles which may trip someone, well away from glass doors.

If you have glass shower enclosures, it is especially important to keep the bathroom floor dry. Use non-skid rugs or mats. Use a suction-cup bath mat or rough-surfaced adhesive strips to give solid footing in the tub or shower stall. Install hand rails for support.

Source: *Because You Care for Kids*, Child Safety: U.S. Consumer Product Safety Commission, Washington, D.C.20207.

Chapter 6

NURSING HOMES

Finding a nursing home will be one of the hardest and most discouraging things that you will do. When I started the search, I was given the names of three homes in the area that provided care for Alzheimer's patients. Not all facilities do provide the type of service that is needed and some do not want Alzheimer's patients.

The first facility that I visited was a large building that reminded me of a fourth-class European hotel. On entering the lobby, I noticed a reception desk, a lounge with chairs (arm to arm around the wall) and a dining room with tables for four (decorated with dusty, faded plastic flowers). The receptionist, who knew I was coming, took me to the third floor where some Alzheimer's patients were housed.

It was crowded on the elevator (one of two) with patients coming and going from their timed assignments in the dining room. The elevator was full of old people and when it stopped, several started to get off, only to be pulled back by an attendant who told them that this was not their floor. Several other patients thought they were going to lunch.

I was confused and depressed before I ever hit the third floor. When the elevator stopped, several other people tried to get off and some tried to get on. The third-floor ward consisted of a lobby with a nursing station, a fifty-centimetre TV and approximately fifteen chairs lined up against the wall. Half the patients were seated in such a way that they were unable to see the TV and the other half weren't watching it anyway. An elderly man was sitting in the middle in a chair getting a haircut. There was also a strong odour which I knew wasn't Lysol or Mr. Clean.

Two halls extended from the nursing station to the patients' bedrooms. A luxury accommodation was a two-bed unit. Most rooms had three or four beds separated by curtains. No home furnishings were allowed, and there was no opportunity for privacy or dignity.

I got the feeling that nothing matched in the whole place. The furniture was of a nondescript nature and looked as if it was about ready to be delivered to St. Vincent de Paul for refurbishing. The colour coordination must have been decided upon by a penal-institution manager and could only be described (as Aila would say) as elephant-breath brown.

I ran — did not walk — to the nearest exit, opened the door to escape so as to avoid the elevator and set off an alarm bell that created more activity than I could have imagined. Two attendants blocked me on the stairs, and after deciding that I didn't belong there, told me never to use the stairs again, that I must wait for the elevator. I conveyed to them, in my best Anglo-Saxon body language, that they need not be concerned, I would never return.

The second nursing home I visited, several days later (after recovering from the first one), was a one-storey building that was bright and clean. I made an appointment to be taken on a tour and found the facility to be a vast improvement over the first nursing home I had visited. The building was constructed in a square with an atrium in the middle that contained a large garden with wide paths and benches. The dining room was attractive in bright colours as was the large recreation area. The patients' rooms were placed on the outside walls around the square and were attractive and bright. There was limited space available for one-bedroom occupancy and most of the rooms contained two, three or four patients. There was no special core for Alzheimer's patients but the ones I observed looked well dressed and were clean and happy.

The third and most impressive nursing home was the Oak Bay Kiwanis Pavilion. It had an honest-to-goodness Alzheimer's unit that was designed and staffed by trained professionals. When I entered the door, I knew I was in for something different. There were fresh flowers in the lobby, paintings on the wall and colours that were bright and happy. I guess I must have looked lost because Jane Peterson, the Social Activity Director, asked if she could help. She informed me that there were no formal tours of the facility that day but she took pity on me and said, "Oh, come on, I have time."

The first floor has two wings, each with its own glassed sun room, a dining room and lounge. In the centre of the building is a large meeting/recreation room and a library with a real fireplace. The second floor, the Alzheimer's ward has two wings, a central dining room, a television lounge and a large recreation room with a piano and audiotape player. Leading from this room is a large porch that, during the summer, often seconds as a dining room with umbrella tables. The large garden on the first floor offers an opportunity for all of the residents to engage in growing flowers and vegetables if they wish. Numerous varieties of roses provide pleasure for all.

All of this was impressive but the most impressive of all was the quality of care I observed, and the professionalism of the staff. Needless to say, I was impressed and continue to have great confidence in the quality of care that Aila is receiving.

When I returned home, I called the social worker from the Ministry of Health and told her that I would wait for an opening at the Oak Bay Kiwanis Pavilion. I had been told that the wait for an opening may be from six to twelve months and so our life settled into a routine of waiting.

The wait, however, was not a year. Three months after being placed on the waiting-list, I received a call from the Oak Bay Kiwanis Pavilion telling me that they had an opening for Aila. I asked how soon they would like Aila to be admitted to the nursing home and they suggested that Friday would be a good time (today was Wednesday!). I was stunned. I didn't expect it — but then I am not sure that I would have ever expected it whenever it came. All I could think of was, I won't have Aila to take care of. What will I do? For her sake, I knew that a decision had to be made. In talking to Louise Johnson, who had called me from the Oak Bay Kiwanis Pavilion, I asked if they would have an opening at a later date. She indicated, kindly but firmly, that she didn't know when the next opening would come. She said it could be a week, it could be three months or it could be a year. There was no possibility of knowing at that time. I asked her if she would hold the room for a day and I would call her back. She understood my problem and said she would. That night I thought of several things. I thought about Aila and her needs, I thought about my needs and I thought: What would be best for her? What happens if I turn down this chance and there isn't another chance for a year? At what stage of development will she be in at that point? I didn't have an answer to that so the next day I called our doctor and told him the situation. His response was that at Aila's age, the disease would probably progress rapidly. It was probably best to put her in a nursing home where I knew she would get good care that would satisfy both Aila and me; I didn't want to have to make a decision in a crisis situation that neither of us would find acceptable and possibly be forced to put her in any institution, because of the severity of the disease.

I called back Louise Johnson the next day and asked her if it was possible for me to bring Aila in on Monday instead of Friday. I thought that it would at least give me the weekend. I must say it was the worst weekend I ever spent. You are filled with doubt as to whether you are doing the right thing, you feel guilty as hell because you are giving up the primary care of the person you love, and I wavered between whether I could let Aila go or not let her go. After talking with the children, I finally came to the decision that we had no choice. If I wanted to be sure that Aila had the best care and the best facilities available, I couldn't take a chance and play roulette with her comfort. I decided to take her to the nursing home on Monday.

Monday came, I told Aila that we were going to a very nice hospital, for a short period of time, where they were going to help her with her Alzheimer's disease. She seemed to be happy with that. She asked if I would come to see her and I said, "Of course, I will be there every day." She asked if it was far away and I said, "No, I could be there in fifteen minutes from our house." This seemed to satisfy her and she seemed to think it was quite reasonable. We packed and I took a few paintings for her. She wanted to know why the paintings were going with her and I said, "Just to make you feel more at home, that I am there, that everything is OK." This she accepted.

Once at the Pavilion, we went upstairs to her room and we unpacked her things. She was introduced to the head nurse and the health-care worker who would be with her for the next couple of days. She was taken around to see where the lounges and television were. She was asked if she would like a cup of tea with a couple of the other ladies. Everything seemed to be going well.

I left at that point and I think cried for probably the next five days. I wondered how I could survive and function, how I could wake up in the morning reach over and not have Aila sleeping next to me, how I would miss the smell of her perfume on the pillow. The nights and the mornings were the hardest because I had time to think and measure my loss. I had lost someone who is still there but unretrievable. There are many times in life when one cries — sometimes happy times, sometimes sad times — but I think that losing someone in this way is the worst emotional trauma of all. The only way I can describe it to myself is as a period of time when the soul cries. It seems that every muscle and fibre of your being cries with you and it hurts.

I will always be thankful that Alyson Hawksworth was the head nurse on the floor that week. I think she knew the turmoil that Aila and I were both going through, Aila not as aware as I but still aware. She performed an amazing act of kindness that I will never forget nor be able to match. She called me every morning for the first week at about 7:30 am and told me what kind of a night Aila had had, what she had been doing the previous afternoon and how she was doing. I can never thank her enough for her kindness.

Don't Leave

Don't leave my love, not yet.
What will I do without you?
Who will share my thoughts?
Who will I laugh with?
Who will hold me and love me on
cold winter evenings when the windows
are iced and the sheets snow?
Who will share our dreams if you go?

Give me your hand.
Don't leave, not yet.
Don't leave.
Please!

Arthur Olson

Evaluation of a Nursing Home

A number of factors went through my mind as I was trying to decide what was best for Aila in a home away from home. I thought, If I were living in a nursing home, what would I like, because I think that Aila and I would like the same things. Where would you be comfortable and where would your loved one be comfortable? There are some specifics, however, that you need to look for:

1. The first thing you can note when you walk through the doors of the nursing home is the cleanliness and safety of the institution. Does it look and smell clean? One of the things you should do is to ask to see the kitchen and bathroom facilities. In the Oak Bay Kiwanis Pavilion, each room has its own toilet and sink and there are several areas for baths to be given to the patients by health-care workers.

2. Find out how much it will cost you and what is covered. Know what you will have to pay for. Will you have to pay for medications or medical activities such as a podiatrist or optometrist? I think

you will be amazed at the small costs that are added on in any home-care facility. They are not large but they add up to anywhere from about $25 to $30 a month. I think that this should be expected and isn't unreasonable.

3. Do the health-care workers understand what is involved in dementia? Do they get constant training? Are the head nurses on the floor specialists in dementia? Thank God, for my sake and Aila's, the nurses at Oak Bay Kiwanis Pavilion are specialists in the area and the health-care workers have training and continuous workshops in the process of working with Alzheimer's patients.

4. What kind of help is given? Is there enough staffing available? What is the ratio of health-care workers to patients? What is the ratio of nurses to patients? Is there an around-the-clock nurse on the Alzheimer's floor. Is there an around-the-clock health-care worker aid on the floor? What kind of facilities are available for them? Is there medical support available? Is there a doctor on call at all times?

5. In most cases the Alzheimer's patient is going to require some kind of medication. You want to be very sure that you know what kind of precautions are taken for the administration of the medication and you want to know who is responsible for providing the medication. It should be a registered nurse who provides the service, at a minimum.

6. What kind of requirements and standards are set up for the nursing home? Compare those standards against what you observe.

7. In case of medical emergencies what kind of support is available? If there is an emergency, what is done? Who is called? You want to be sure that the nursing home has a good idea where you can be found at all times of the day. If you are going to leave the

area for a short trip you need to inform them
where you can be contacted or provide them with a
name of someone who can speak for you in your
absence.

8. What safety precautions are available in the building to ensure that the Alzheimer's patient is safe?
What standards are set up by the governing boards?

You will probably be asked to sign some papers when the
patient is admitted to the home. You should be very sure that
you understand what these documents mean and that you
have read them thoroughly. If you have any questions concerning what is written, ask questions of the administration of
the nursing home, or if you wish to have more information,
you may contact your family lawyer to clarify what legal
responsibilities are attached to the documents you are signing.

All good facilities that take care of Alzheimer's patients will
have waiting-lists. You are the primary caregiver and guardian
of the patient and need to be aware of what kind of care
model you wish to see employed in the nursing home to
which you are entrusting your loved one. Table 2 is a check-list
of practices that might help you in your decision. There are
two basic facility models, the custodial and the psychosocial.
There is no question that the psychosocial model is the one
that I want to see in operation for the care of Aila.

Table 2. A Checklist of Practices to be Considered in Designing the Psychosocial Model of Care

STAFF WITH RESIDENTS

Custodial Model	Psychosocial Model
Staff view their role as one of caretaker, thus being in control and doing for residents rather than helping them manage as much as possible for themselves.	Staff function as enablers and friends of residents, encouraging them to assume as much control as possible over their own lives.
Staff function according to a prescribed job description.	Staff are willing and are encouraged by their supervisor to extend their responsibilities beyond the specified job description to improve the quality of life of residents.
In order to get tasks done quickly, staff do things for residents that they may be able to do for themselves.	They spend time and effort encouraging residents to maintain independence and manage self-care.
They categorize residents as 'patients' and consider all patients as having basically the same needs and limitations.	They become aware of residents as individuals with worth and potential and with individual needs.
Staff see the resident as someone different from themselves because he or she is labeled as a patient and is institutionalized.	Staff relate to residents as friends and enablers valuing each person as an individual.
They have little communication with residents when giving treatments, helping them eat, or assisting them with bathing.	Staff reduce the distance between the staff and residents by sharing activities and by communicating with residents frequently.
Staff find uniforms necessary as evidence of rank and being in control.	Staff find that wearing street clothes helps to eliminate the hospital-like climate and reduces the separation between staff and residents.

THE RESIDENT

Custodial Model	Psychosocial Model
Residents fulfill the only role available to them — that of dependent, needy, sick patients.	Residents maintain some control over their lives and continue in normal social roles to the extend possible.
The resident has no legitimate way of behaving that merits recognition and so becomes essentially a non-person.	Recognition and feedback are provided to acknowledge residents' achievements.
They find that the only outlet for them is to behave in abnormal ways; in fact, they soon realize that "sick" behavior is expected by staff and more acceptable to them than wellness.	Each resident is a person in his own right with his or her own likes and dislikes, abilities and needs, and the focus is on the 'wellness' in each individual.
Residents are all seen as alike — old and sick — without taking into account individual differences.	Individuality is recognized and encouraged.

THE PHYSICAL ENVIRONMENT

Custodial Model	Psychosocial Model
The facility follows the design of the medical mode, emphasizing that the residents are ill and in an institution.	The Setting offers a homelike environment, reinforcing feelings of wellness, involvement and belonging.
The setting is sterile and areas are undistinguishable.	Colours and artifacts are used for stimulation and interest and to accommodate sensory loss.
Doors are locked or residents are controlled by physical or chemical restraints.	Safety measures are used by they are designed to ensure maximum freedom of residents.
Sleeping rooms are furnished uniformly with a minimum of personal belongings.	Sleeping rooms are furnished with each individual's furniture and personal possessions to provide continuity with his or her earlier life.
Residents have few opportunities for privacy.	Baths and toilets are designed to ensure privacy and staff members knock before entering individual sleeping rooms.

THE PROGRAM OF DAILY ACTIVITIES

Custodial Model	*Psychosocial Model*
Programming may be sporadic or nonexistent; life is usually devoid of any activity resembling a life style on the outside.	The day's activities are designed to include everyone and planned to meet the needs of individual residents.
Even scheduled activities are cancelled frequently.	Programs are consistent and predictable, although some activities are introduced spontaneously to respond to needs and relieve tension.
With the exception of the activity therapist, staff take little or no part in the activities for residents.	Staff, themselves, are involved in the programs and activities.
Activities of daily living are seen as necessities and something to complete as soon as possible, with staff doing the major part of the tasks involved in order to meet the daily schedule.	Activities of daily living are seen as opportunities for staff to share with residents and occasions to help them continue to function as well as possible.
Staff give little support to the activity therapist and may, in fact, consider activities non-essential and a nuisance.	Staff place value on activities which improve the quality of life of residents and enable them to continue activities and interests of their earlier lives.
Planned activities are often childish, degrading for adults, and repetitive, serving only as 'busy work'.	Activities are centered around a goal, are appropriate for adults, and are valued and stimulating.
Staff become impatient with residents who have their own interests and friends, and prefer them to the institution's activities.	Staff encourage independence and initiative on the part of residents

THE STAFF WITH CO-WORKERS

Custodial Model	*Psychosocial Model*
Staff are interested in maintaining status and being the sole possessors of knowledge.	They share knowledge and information with other staff.
They exercise control through criticism.	They help others recognize successes and give others support by giving positive feedback.
Staff give little or no support to co-workers (e.g. nursing staff to activity therapists and vice-versa).	Staff recognize the value of the work of others and give support and help.
They hand down orders giving little or no opportunity for the sharing of problems and successes among various staff levels.	They share with staff at all levels in problem-solving and helping to develop plans.

Source; Dorothy H. Coons & Lena Metzelaar, The University of Michigan.

Costs

Canada

The cost of living in a nursing home in Canada is usually set by the provincial Ministry of Health and generally covers approximately seventy-five per cent of the basic expenses. In British Columbia, for example, you can expect that the Old Age Pension plus the Canadian Pension Plan will cover the costs of most facilities.

There are, however, great variations from one nursing home to another. At the Oak Bay Kiwanis Pavilion, for example, all of the rooms are private and assessed to the family for $21.40 a day (January 1991). The British Columbia Ministry of Health contributes $62.00 per day, resulting in a total of $83.40. At the other two nursing homes I visited, the rooms with four beds were assessed at $83.00 per day with single rooms costing approximately $105.00 per day. The two and three-bed rooms were assessed proportionally. On a per diem basis, the cost to the individual, depending on the facility, can vary greatly. The cost is not necessarily related to the quality of care. The care of the individual in a one-bed room at $21.40 per day is probably far superior to that in a four-bed room for the same cost.

Additional expenses added on to the basic cost for the facility need to be known before a decision is made. In some nursing homes additional assessments may be made for religious services, entertainment services, physiotherapists, dental checks and other services. Some of these additional costs may be reasonable and acceptable, others may appear to be a scam.

United States

Nursing-home care is expensive. In order to make a decision in respect to this kind of care, it is important that all aspects of the financial costs be considered. There are basically three possible ways of receiving some aid so that the total financial burden does not fall upon the family. The first of these options is private insurance, the second is the Veterans' Administration and the third is Medicare.

Private insurance is certainly a valuable asset to have if it covers dementing illnesses. Many people who have paid high fees for health insurance are surprised when they find that nursing care and nursing-home care are not covered in their policies. In some cases the cost may be covered for a short period of time, but certainly not for the length of time required by Alzheimer's disease. It is wise to check your policy and request specific information on the coverage for long-term care. The effect of not having made specific inquiry could be a great financial burden.

The Veterans' Administration or the nearest Veterans' Hospital should be able to provide you with information that may be of help in aiding a loved one inflicted with Alzheimer's disease, if he is a veteran. It is also possible that, in some situations, dependants of veterans may be able to receive some benefits.

Medicare, in some cases, may pay for part of nursing-home care for a limited period of time. A serious problem may arise when a person who has Medicare finds that funding provides nursing-home care for only several weeks, not for the extended long-time care needed by the Alzheimer's patient. For some, the program is a cruel joke.

Medicare is a federally funded program; applications are made through local Social Security offices. The regulations are complex and should be thoroughly investigated by a call or visit to the Social Security office.

There are two parts to Medicare, parts A and B. People are eligible for part A if they are sixty-five or over, if they have received Social Security Disability for twenty-four months or are receiving Social Security or Railroad Retirement, or if they pay for the coverage. People who are eligible for part A are also eligible for part B if they pay the premium.

Most Alzheimer's patients need custodial care not skilled care. The distinction is significant in respect to cost. Skilled care is defined as meaning that the patient needs continuous care or service from a registered nurse or practical nurse (licensed) or must meet the requirements for rehabilitation. Also, Medicare cannot be activated until after the person has been admitted to a nursing home following discharge from a hospital.

Given all of these factors, that in many cases are not applicable to the person involved, the stay in a nursing home at Medicare cost is limited. After a maximum of one hundred days, additional funding must be found. It is no wonder that the survivors (caregivers) may find themselves financially destitute when their loved ones die. The combination of concern for the loved one and for her own financial future as the survivor is emotionally devastating.

Nurse in Charge — A Dialogue

The head nurse on the floor of the Alzheimer's ward is a very important person, not because of her authority but because of the tone she establishes for the living environment of your loved one. The following is a conversation with Irene Barnes, head nurse, friend, and all-around good gal. Her insights and humanity are of help to me and I hope they can be to you.

What do you see as your role when a patient comes to stay at the Oak Bay Kiwanis Pavilion?

"As the person in charge of the unit, I think my role starts before the resident actually comes here and that is when family members come to visit on the tour. It's important to view the facility before you choose it to see if you believe in the philosophy of the place — such as our belief of non-restraint and as little medication as possible, maximum utilization of facilities etc. It's really important to come on a tour and see the whole layout of the facility and ask as many questions as you can. You meet me and know that I will be looking after your relatives when they come and you get some sense of who will be responsible in taking over their care. Once you have decided to come here, then, my role becomes one of informing you of what is happening and gleaning all the information I can about the resident and the family members because the more I know, the better able I am to help my staff understand the situation, utilize the abilities that the person still has, find things to stimulate people.

"Because the disease is an unlearning process, things that occurred in their childhood could trigger good memories, and this is what I need to know — a social history is helpful. Your expectations are really important for me to know. If the environment is the best possible, quite often, the family members get false hope and think that the disease has stopped or is going away and things will get better. It is important that no matter how good things look right now, the disease still is there and things do change. I like to make sure that families are aware and that when they do see changes occurring — it is not a sudden shock and they don't say, 'Why didn't you warn me that this would happen?'

"A lot of decisions have to be made. How much intervention do you have to do? Finishing off business with the family member. And also to help you as a family member still out in society start the letting go — the grieving process because the person you know has gone and you have to start building your own life. If you can start taking little steps now, when death comes the transition is better. I do a lot of counselling and talking. I welcome any question. I don't always know the right answer but if I don't then maybe I can find someone who can help you. The history is important.

"You need to be aware of what is happening on the unit too. Sometimes you will come and see things that are distressing — why is this going on and why is this approach being used? Don't ever leave feeling uncomfortable or in doubt. It is best to ask and talk about what you see so you can sort it out and what it is we are doing here 'cause we really have the personnel for it. We acknowledge whatever reality they are in at the moment. If, like Aila, their memories are in wartime, hearing bombs falling and they are on the floor in the fetal position to protect themselves, there is no way you are going to get them off the floor so we acknowledge that and make sure that they are protected until they come through that episode and are back with us. The big thing is acknowledging their reality when they have a episodic moment. Many of our residents suffer from dementia and occasionally we get information from what they say, benefit from it and pass it on with the good observations to the family. When you have so many heavy things to deal with it is nice to have a few little gems to store and remember. Certainly I tend to not burden you with the negatives that are happening. You know them. If I see that you are getting unrealistic expectations then I will certainly try and talk to you.

"One of the things that impresses me is the family dynamics that occur here. Whatever involvement you want with your family member in our care, we acknowledge and accept it. No one is forced to do anything that they don't want to. If they don't want to come, then that is okay. But we still let you know what is happening. We look for things like clothing, wheelchairs, things like this to help make the stay for the person a little bit more comfortable. Some things we can't provide and we will let you know. Again if you can't supply them that's okay too, we will work around it. If families wish to be more involved, we definitely have our care conferences, ongoing consultations with us. It is nice to come for activities. It is hard to sit and talk with someone who is really not able to carry on a conversation but it makes things better if you go to an activity downstairs and you can both enjoy the concert or dinner party. It is always nice to see them at their best and we try and make them look good especially when they go downstairs. We encourage families to make this their home too. There is no restriction on visiting times. You can sit in the dining room and have a cup of coffee at the table with them or assist your family member with their meal.

"I find that when residents first come to us with the mild dementias it is okay to still go out for rides but when they start getting into the more severe stages, it is too traumatic for them to leave the unit. It is hard because you want to take them to your home but they can't remember it and it just makes things more difficult.

"That is another hurdle, another loss that family members have to deal with. That is the stage when we quite often see them breaking off their visits. The involvement is too painful for them, they just stop coming period. "We do have a geriatric consultant available, family doctors will look after your family member but we do have him available. If I have a problem, I can refer to him instantly but it's definitely the decision of the family and the doctor.

"My role quite often is one of an advocate for the resident. Just because you are elderly and have dementia doesn't mean you still can't feel pain; sometimes surgery is put off because they think the person doesn't feel the pain. Quite often we have to put pressure on the system to get it done. When we are successful, I feel we have won a battle, which is great."

Chapter 7

INSIDE THE NURSING HOME,
TALKING WITH TWO PROFESSIONALS

During the time that we are the primary caregivers of our loved ones, we are very sensitive to their welfare and comfort. When they enter the nursing home, however, much of our responsibility is transferred to a new group of caregivers. How they are taking care of our wife, husband or other relative can only be observed by our visits or conversations with those charged with their care.

Following are two discussions that provided me with many insights into the care of Aila and the philosophy that operates in caregiving. The first is with Alyson Hawksworth. You, too, should take the time and make the effort to know what is going on inside.

"Aila's first couple of months with us on the unit contained many unique and challenging moments. From the beginning she was the focus of much creative problem solving. She challenged us, not only as caregivers, but as people who saw in her many character traits that we admired and respected: determination, directness, humour and intellect. We were challenged to create for her an environment where she would feel safe. Her first months were spent living the experiences of World War II; the anxiety she demonstrated was probably due to the great fear of the war that she was experiencing. We felt great empathy for the young woman who was held captive and terrorized in her own city.

"Aila was unique in that physically she was experiencing thyroid dysfunction, the effects of which could further have heightened her fears and anxiety. Identifying and following through with a very special medical course of action was a new and learning experience for all our staff — professional and nonprofessional. The treatment was one which our facility had never experienced so staff education, support and clarification was a focus as well."

What about the medication of Alzheimer's patients?

"Here, our philosophy is less is best. What we found works the best is a natural routine — good food, lots to drink, never being constipated, fresh air, physical activity in fresh air. That is why winters are particular challenges for staff; it is often raining and you simply can't go out, so we are sure that the patient has those five things: sleep, rest, enough to drink, not being constipated and regular movements. Having a normal body cycle is wonderful stabilization. Having undisturbed sleep at night when incontinence becomes part of care is important. If the bed is very wet and a dry bed is warranted, it is as smooth a change as possible."

Do all the patients go through an aggressive stage?

"Most residents experience aggressive times and staff are taught nursing interventions to effectively deal with agitation and its expression. Simply put, residents are allowed to experience those emotions while the focus of the staff is to be sure that no resident is in a vulnerable position so that they might get physically hurt. Staff distract and redirect to diffuse the high energy. Often, once the anger/energy is released, the episode is over. It is important to remember to look for physical, environmental or social clues that could lead to the expression of anger. If a cause (i.e. ill-fitting shoes pressing on a corn, or feeling too hot, a too noisy environment etc.) is identified to explain the behaviour, it is important to take action to solve it as appropriate and to relay this information to other nursing staff so that the factors leading up to an incident will not be repeated.

"Active problem solving combined with *actual caring attitudes* forms the most effective nursing environment, on a unit such as this.

"Aila's expression of fear was exhibited by constant calling out for a staff member to be with her. As a staff, we learned to reassure her and support each other while medical and nursing courses of care were planned and acted upon. It could not have been an easy time for her and we felt relieved that her short- term memory was not intact, so that our failures were not apparent to her.

"Often, the most effective nursing response/action was to embrace Aila and hold her — a quiet, gentle embrace relaxed her and helped her feel safe. This worked more often than it didn't — not very scientific but very caring."

Disturbed Dreams

What memories chase us?
What dreams do we conjure?
Childhood remembrances of things gone wrong.
What memories chase us?

Rest quietly my love,
The old memories do not count.
They are figments of our conscience,
They do not count.
They are not real.

Reality is held jointly, you and I.
Your devils are mist,
They hold no meaning in our lives,
They are unreal, only we are real.
                                        Arthur Olson

"I think the most important part of my job when someone comes to live in the unit is to not only look at where the resident is in their disease but also where the family is in their acceptance of the person coming to a facility. I'm very conscious of how my staff and myself can support the family in being where they are in the acceptance of the illness or helping them move to the next phase if that is where they are ready to go."

How do you determine that?

"A lot of times, it is the level of concern expressed by a family member. A husband may be very upset that his wife's not wearing a bra. That's his focus. At four o'clock every day, I know he is going to be there to visit his wife. It's physically uncomfortable for his wife to go through the process of putting on a bra each day. She resists it and it ends up being a most upsetting behaviour for her. The staff's focus is to be gentle and not force. It's obvious he doesn't hear what I am saying even though I am explaining our position — it still doesn't make any difference to him. He doesn't appear to accept where his loved one is in the development of the disease.

"Another example is sometimes when you encourage the family to interact with the staff. Let us know what it is you want. For instance, when I met your daughter, I felt she heard what I was saying and I think she felt that I heard her. I don't know if that meant she was very intelligent, better acquainted, or more accepting of her mother's illness.

"When I met with your son, I felt he was hurting more visibly than your daughter. She covered it up better than he did. That is all okay, that is where they were in their grief course."

As the person's illness progresses, how do you help the husband or wife understand what is happening? The person sees things they may not understand.

"In the care set-up we have formal times to discuss the progress of the disease, where the patient is in the process, and how the new resident is reacting to care. At six weeks we will do that, again at three months, then six months — we will meet with the family, the dietitian, the activity person, member of the staff, plus myself, and in some cases the doctor is very keen to be part of that formal meeting. Other than that, I depend a lot on the health-care workers to give me information as to how the family are doing. Sometimes people come every day and then don't come any more or they stop communicating. It is extremely important to keep the communication channels open. I always hold families as being perfectly able and capable of dealing with whatever I say because they have everything, whereas the resident has nothing. It is very important that I respect the family for being all together and even if they are grieving inappropriately, in my opinion, it still is where they are and that is where they need to be."

What would you say is inappropriate grieving?

"I guess it would be for a husband or wife to come and spend a couple of hours per shift and the whole time that they are there be after the staff to do this and that and tell them they are not doing a good enough job. You meet with a person two or three times to talk about where the person is in the disease and it doesn't make any difference. They go back to square one and might not even have anything to do with this facility. They need more help than I can give them and what often makes me feel very frustrated and very defeated is that I can't help them. I honestly can't and they are not helping themselves because they are stuck back in the gate. In that way it is inappropriate but right for that person 'cause that is the way they are dealing with the problem. We understand their concern."

One of the things I remember, that I am sure put a lot of pressure on you, was the first week that Aila came in.

"Aila was a very, very interesting person because her social skills were so intact. The support she had at home was obviously one hundred and fifty per cent. When you spent an hour with her you realized, Oh, there is something going on here. There aren't very many people admitted with the same intactment as she and that blew us away. We weren't used to that; we were used to people who were definitely, obviously incapable. They couldn't carry on a conversation; it was obvious they could do nothing. And yet she was saying, 'Fine, thank you.' Her social skills and manners were excellent and it wasn't until she had been with us for almost two weeks that we realized that it was a cover-up. As the social support that she had at home wasn't with her any more, it just all crumpled away; she became very afraid and she yelled all the louder. In order to support herself, she was very dictatorial and autocratic and our staff was still in the phase of, Gosh, does she really need to be here? They were kind of inbetwixt and inbetween because I don't remember ever having anyone who camouflaged as well. I remember staff meetings, where they would say, 'Aila was particularly insistent on such-and-such and I am getting really tired and worn down.' How can we as a staff deal with this?

"Aila at times was all right in her room. She was quiet in there. If she was the only one making a noise, I guess that was all right, but when her balance started to go, when she started not walking very well, I think that frightened her even more. That is natural. If you don't feel that you are standing very straight that would explain why her anxiety was so much."

Do you find a difference in the way families react to people who are quite old, say mothers and fathers in their seventies and eighties, compared to someone quite young who has the disease?

"Very much so. The older person is a lot more peaceful. The younger ones have been typically active, verbally abusive. Their agitation, disease symptomology is that much more pronounced. I think the statement is the younger they are, the rougher the course in their disease. The more pronounced the aggression, the longer it is, the more energy involved. Whereas the older person tends to be more peaceful, forgetful, not knowing and not caring. Their level of energy is one quarter of the younger person's."

The following is the discussion with Irene Barnes:

There is a special atmosphere on this floor. How is it created?

"That is a special project that I have been working on for two years, an educational component. In teaching the staff, we made them aware of what it is like to have visual disturbances, hearing disturbances and not be able to reply. It really made a big difference. They now literally treat every resident as if they could reply appropriately and certainly the patients respond. It is also one of intervention in the sense that there is no need for aggression. If you are doing something to me dealing with anger, what makes you angry? If they are starting to get angry, you just back off and see what is happening in this whole big picture. What am I doing to the resident? Are they too hot? Are they sick? Are they constipated? Are they thirsty? You look at the whole thing that can trigger off the cycle, they become more observant and aware of who and what they feel when they come on to the unit. If you are in a bad state of mind from a family problem at home, your residents will reflect it. I call this unit 'mirror' of who we are and the residents are a mirror of who you are today. That's why we really push for soothing, relaxing music, nonextrastimulating music. It drives the staff members crazy but it 'detones' the residents. You can tell a new staff member because they don't react the same as regular staff members do, they are louder, they are moving faster, they are kind of rushing the residents a bit more and they talk above the music whereas the rest of us are now so used to it so we don't react to it.

"Backing off, if you (the patient) are not ready right now I'll come back in five minutes. Because you are dealing with short-term-memory loss you don't remember what was occurring five minutes ago, or two minutes ago. We really cash in on that a lot. Sometimes we all have our idiosyncrasies about certain people, and if one person isn't dealing with a situation very well, then get someone else to step in. I use that a lot. So-and-so is in a kind of different space today, why don't you see what you can do. Usually someone can diffuse the problem."

I noticed that Aila didn't like Rosa across the hall to come into her room. Now Rosa comes in and adjusts her blanket on her legs and pats her head and Aila is very happy. Once in a while she will look over and say, "Is Mother over there?"

"Residents learn to support each other. We are role models and when they see what we're doing they follow through. They see us hugging residents and patting them. When you are hurting, it is nice to have someone hold your hand, pat you on the shoulder. Because your wife and Rosa are always there, the staff members change, but residents are always there, they come to depend on each other, the bond grows over a length of time so they feel very safe as long as the other person is there."

How do you maintain the morale of the staff when the demands are so high and the turnover of personnel is great?

"One of the things I look at is to enjoy the blessing that each resident gives us today. You are refocusing your pleasures. Our residents, no matter how much care you give them, do not look one-hundred-per-cent great all the time. You can have them leave their room looking great and smelling like a rose and in ten minutes you have disaster on your hands. You can't look at that as a reward, but when they do look good and someone acknowledges it, 'Oh, Mother looks so good today, thank you.'

"Focusing on different things for reward. I certainly see my staff as an extension of myself. I like to know what space they are in when you come into work in the morning. Usually when I get reports from staff I want to hear about something good that happened to that resident today — not just negative reporting. Education is a wonder. If you understand what is happening to the resident then you won't set them up for false expectations. A lot of my time is spent on instant education.

"Dealing with their own issues. When someone reacts violently and is quite upset about something, the resident isn't the problem — it is your reaction. Let's look at what is going on here. How do you deal with anger? Are you from a background of abuse and somebody hits you and then that whole case comes back? I tend to stop and look at what is going on in that area too and talk about it. Pass on all the information I can get on what is happening with Alzheimer's research. Looking at family dynamics — our residents react positively to certain family members and negatively to others. Staff can become confused. The dynamics and the negativity they feel and observe can be taken out of context inappropriately and incorrect interpretations made. Staff then has to be aware of this possibility, step back and acknowledge what is happening, realize that the anger is not personally directed at them.

"On the weekends we draw names and exchange gifts first thing in the morning. Who wants to work on the weekend? Most of us are on diets, so we try to cut back on the goodies that we bring in. If there is a birthday we acknowledge that with some sort of treat. If things are going well and we are fully staffed we draw a name and let someone go home early if everything is up to date. But it also means on the next day, Sunday, we focus on passing on information, making sure our clothes are organized, our rooms are sorted out — it's ongoing. We try to promote things like staff association parties and the little raffles that we have downstairs. We are going to have a Christmas party up here, Hallowe'en parties and dress-up days. Our residents can't give us that much back, but we still have to give them a lot. If I can have a few moments for them then it makes a difference. Right now, we are having weekly meetings with our staff. We have to stay within the thirty-minute structure, but that's about all the time I can schedule to get them off the unit. They know that if something is bothering them, they know that they are going to have thirty minutes of our time. I work very hard to have someone covering the unit so we don't have to worry about our residents being taken care of. Let them be involved in the whole process of running the unit. If it isn't working very well, what is the alternative, give me some ideas and brainstorm with everyone. Sometimes it doesn't work, sometimes it does. Let them be involved."

Is there anything else you think it would be important for people to know?

"There are a few things of which I think family members should be aware. One is that family members need to ask questions. They shouldn't leave the unit concerned about anything or upset by a situation that they have seen or in which they have been involved. They need to deal with every issue as it comes up. Quite often they will find that there is a very good reason for everything that is happening, even though it may not make sense to them.

"It is important that families realize that we accept whatever they can give to their resident or family member. Some family members can visit daily, others can only come once a year and we accept whatever it is they are able to give.

"It's time to look after yourself as a caregiver. In the home, quite often, our family members have been totally exhausted and the load has been lightened by bringing their family members to the facility. We will look after that part of the burden, even though they are greatly involved in the care. But it is very important that they start looking after themselves and refurbish their depleted resources.

"Staff have found humour as a wonderful way to lighten the load on the unit. Quite often it can be nonsensical and at times to outside people it may look out of place but this is a terribly serious disease and the caregiving load is very heavy. We need to make it lighter."

Chapter 8

THE OAK BAY KIWANIS PAVILION

Entrusting your loved one to the care of others is a heart-rending and vitally important decision. There is no room for error. I could not be happier with the decision I made for Aila, and so I am describing the Oak Bay Kiwanis Pavilion to give you a picture that will serve as a measure for you if your time to make a decision should come. Much of what you read here is based upon the videotape *Love Is Not Enough* prepared by the Pavilion staff.

Introduction

The Oak Bay Kiwanis Pavilion, in Victoria, British Columbia, Canada, is a 121-bed, intermediate-care facility administering to the needs of the frail elderly. The increasing number of residents admitted with cognitive impairment resulted in the development of a forty-one-bed Special Needs Unit with outdoor patios, door-surveillance systems and special activity programs.

Residents with dementias present unique care problems requiring creative solutions that prevent disruption in the delivery of care.

Progressive loss of memory and intellect, together with distortions, i.e. images and sounds, can cause misunderstanding and anxiety for the older person.

For these people, life inexorably begins to slip out of focus.[1]

These residents frequently present the following characteristics:

- loss of learning ability
- delusions and hallucinations
- loss of memory and orienting abilities
- profound anxiety and fear
- wandering and restlessness
- loss of ability to manage personal care
- unpredictable behaviour

[1] Video *"Love is Not Enough"* Oak Bay Kiwanis Pavilion

- misunderstanding and non-understanding of instructions, resulting in noncompliance
- agitation or withdrawal
- coping behaviours that may not be socially acceptable

...Dementia is a lonely and tortuous road and we can only guess at the feelings of those who travel it. They need the love and support of family and staff. They deserve our understanding and compassion as if we too travelled in their path.[1]

The Oak Bay Kiwanis Pavilion recognized a responsibility to provide a standard of care and programming, using present facilities and staff more creatively, which would result in a more meaningful and dignified quality of life for its residents with dementia and their families.

The staff expressed concern about the rising number of injuries to residents and staff, the increasing care requirements of residents, and the decreasing quality of life for residents. The implementation of a non-restraint policy presented several concerns for resident safety and protection, as well as legal issues. Current medical and nursing literature supports a non-restraint policy emphasizing the overuse, abuse and cost of restraints. In 1988, the Oak Bay Kiwanis Pavilion implemented a Quality Assurance Program. The Pavilion's mission, commitment to residents and policies supported a philosophy of non-restraint. The entire staff became involved, through committees, in assessing current practices and in creating staff-development sessions to deal with non-restraint. The program was actively supported by the administrator, physicians, long-term-care assessors and family members.

They established the Special Care Unit Committee with ad hoc committees based on Standards for Accreditation of Canadian Long-Term-Care Centres as outlined. These are:
1. Goals and Objectives
2. Organization and Staffing
3. Facilities Equipment and Supplies
4. Policies and Procedures
5. Care Program

6. Education
7. Quality Assurance

The staff, with frequent reminders *not to fear reprisal* and constant encouragement to use creativity in providing alternatives, created an environment where it was *okay to take risks*. The registered nurses were role models in implementing creative alternatives to restraint. A program was developed by the in-service coordinator to assist the health-care workers with skills in dealing with the cognitively impaired in a non-restraint environment.

Each change was introduced as a trial; the staff was actively involved in problem solving to create a practical, workable program. These trial periods were crucial to staff acceptance as this change process was less threatening.

Success of the program was evident within a short time. Initially there were more resident falls, but the number of injuries remained the same. The number of falls has now decreased. It is now a geri-chair-free facility. Three residents who were extended care became mobile and remain so five months later. The residents are free to work off excess energy and enjoy their safe environment. The staff has become more comfortable with the policy since observing the results, and the general atmosphere of the unit is one of relaxed friendliness.

Philosophy
The philosophy of the Special Care Unit for residents with dementing illness is to provide a living environment that supports and enhances the existing potential of each resident.

The objective is to reduce fear and anxiety caused by the effects of neurological damage, thus allowing each resident to effectively use his/her remaining skills and abilities. This goal is achieved through the appropriate assessment of dysfunctions and strengths, the use of creative, non-invasive strategies (or interventions) and working in partnership with the families. Under such circumstances people with degenerative dementia appear to thrive.

The creation of a therapeutic, non-threatening world, together with formal caregivers who reach out with specialized skills, ingenuity and respect for each unique individual and his/her family, make it possible for residents with dementing illness to live life to its fullest.

Room 222

I saw her sitting by the bed,
A name no longer on the door,
A sterile vision of someone gone,
Her head bent, intent on images.

She smoothed the bed and placed
Her palms against the picture.
Caressing the one dimensional form.
A sadness in her eyes and the lines of her face.

She looked up when she felt me
Glancing through the open door
And smiled.
As if to say. "You understand."

Caress the image
And smooth the bed.
It is all that is left of Room 222
Until the next.
                    Arthur Olson

STANDARD I   GOALS AND OBJECTIVES

COMPOSITION OF COMMITTEE: Interdisciplinary, to include Administration, Registered Nurses, Health Care Workers and support Staff, i.e., Housekeepers.

PURPOSE OF COMMITTEE: To develop goals and objectives appropriate to a Special Care Unit for residents with dementia and related conditions using Gentlecare[1] concepts.

GOALS	RATIONALE	EFFECT
1. To care for each person as an individual, not as a diagnosis or problem.	*"The challenge of the staff is to discover the unique person behind the dementia."*[2]	Every effort is made to assist independent functioning.
2. To provide a cheerful, supportive, homelike, secure environment which is responsive to human needs[1].	Gwyther says room furnishings and decor should reflect residents[1] past as well as current interests.	*"A secure, interesting environment arranged and supported by staff."*[2]
3. To recognize the contribution of family and community.	Residents need the love and support of family . . . *"They deserve our understanding and compassion as if we too travelled in their paths."*[2]	Family support meetings and involvement in planning as well as implementation of care.
4. To respect and encourage the energy, ideas as well as innovative and creative spirit of staff with regard to resident care.	Involve staff in care decisions. Grant staff a broader range of decision – making. Encourage problem solving within the *Gentlecare*[1] concept.	The quality of life of both the person with the dementing illness and the care giver is directly affected by the *Gentlecare*[1] approach.
5. To understand that "our" reality is not the only reality.	*"Distortions in images and sound lead to confusions, terror and helplessness."*[2]	Gwyther says staff do not use rational explanation, they exhibit support and use diversion to less stressful subject.

Moyra Jones Resources
Video "Love is Not Enough"

STANDARD II   ORGANIZATION AND STAFFING

COMPOSITION OF COMMITTEE: Registered Nurses and Health Care Workers.

PURPOSE OF COMMITTEE: Review current care needs over a twenty – four hour period and design creative methods of meeting these needs within the existing staffing resources.

DECISION	RATIONALE	EFFECT
1. Staff makes two rounds per night instead of three.	Residents sleep better with fewer interruptions.	Disruptive behaviours reduced when residents are rested.
2. One night position transferred to days for bath program.	*"Bathing is an intimate activity. It is difficult, especially for the elderly, to accept help from strangers."*[2]	Problem behaviours associated with bathing are avoided with a consistent staff member in charge.
3. All residents will be bathed during day shift.	To recognize "Sundowning", i.e., increased confusion late in the day." (Gwyther 1985)	*"An attractive environment, regular routine and support create a pleasurable experience."*[2]
4. One staff member responsible to assist with bowel and activation programs.	*"Taking care of one's toilet needs is fundamental to dignity and control."*[2]	Individual needs and habits are considered *"to assist independent functioning".*[2]
5. Staff assignments are changed every two weeks.	To provide new input into each segment of resident care.	Provides variety in resident assignments.
6. Division of labour is determined according to workload measurement indicators.	Each staff member has a manageable workload.	Work satisfaction for staff. More caring behaviours are possible when workload is not frustrating.
7. Special Care Unit staff do not rotate off the unit.	Attitudes toward management of residents with dementia are unique. Special skills are required. Education and personal preference are important for those who achieve these skills.	Staff maintain their skills resulting in better resident care.
8. RN is a clinical leader and a "role model".	Skills are best learned by demonstration and encouragement. "A Head Nurse is a key person to implement change, provide leadership and motivation. (English 1989)	Residents will be exposed to the same continuous courtesy and caring.

Moyra Jones Resources
Video "Love is Not Enough"

STANDARD III   FACILITIES EQUIPMENT AND SUPPLIES

COMPOSITION OF COMMITTEE: Registered Nurses, Health Care Workers, Support and Paramedical Staff.

PURPOSE OF COMMITTEE: Review space utilization, room function and environment with regard to the effects on the residents and the meeting of their needs.

DECISION	RATIONALE	EFFECT
1. Change room aesthetics to meet resident needs.	Individualizing room decor and supplying items of interest help to provide a homelike, satisfying environment.	Clocks at eye level. Multi – textured pictures. Furniture arrangement.
2. Noise level decreased.	*"To reduce the stress of noise".*[2]	Perceptual deficits are less intrusive in a quiet pleasant atmosphere.
3. Change dining room to support quiet social experience. Residents with similar capabilities seated together. Quiet music background. Staff serve and interact with residents to encourage a pleasant experience.	*"Dining is an important principal behaviour . . . and to achieve serenity in the dining room, staff project a sense of calmness and acceptance".*[2]	*"Aberrant behaviours are regarded as eccentricities"*[2] rather than problems, i.e., wandering from table to table, moving chairs, collecting table dishes. Meal service is adapted to individual resident abilities, i.e., finger foods, adapted dinnerware.

Moyra Jones Resources
Video "Love is Not Enough"

STANDARD IV   POLICIES AND PROCEDURES

COMPOSITION OF COMMITTEE: Interdisciplinary to include Administration, Medical Coordinator, Registered Nurses, Health Care Workers, Support and Paramedical Staff.

PURPOSE OF COMMITTEE: To review all policies and procedures to assure relevance and implementation. Special emphasis was on the design and implementation of a nonrestraint program.

DECISION	RATIONALE	EFFECT
1. All modes of physical or mechanical restraint or use of force are no longer care options.	"Particularly troubling are the physical immobility and the emotional destructiveness of fear . . . and loss of self – esteem." (English 1989)	"The search must always be for the cause of the problem, for the appropriate distraction or method of support rather than the use of intrusive strategies such as medications and restraint".[2]
2. Environmental restraints are not used.	Increases the residents' sense of freedom and, thereby, their sense of self as a human being.	Increased physical activity with less disruptive behaviour.
3. Medications reduced from an average of 6 per resident to 2. 1 per resident, including laxatives and vitamins.	Medications have many side effects and interactions.	Residents maintain the highest individual mental and physical state possible.

Moyra Jones Resources
Video "Love is Not Enough"

STANDARD V   CARE PROGRAM

COMPOSITION OF COMMITTEE: Interdisciplinary, to include Administration, Registered Nurses, Health Care Workers and Paramedical Staff.

PURPOSE OF COMMITTEE: To review individual needs, develop plan of care and special programs to meet those needs.

DECISION	RATIONALE	EFFECT
1. Medical Coordinator to consult four hours a week and be available for consultation 24 hours every day.	To identify and manage medical problems of residents when the need arises.	Immediate identification of symptoms and behaviour with a medical basis prevents escalation to crisis.
2. Biweekly pharmacist visits to review and monitor resident drug profiles and experiences and to share in staff education.	"It is imperative that residents be free of chemical as well as physical restraints." (English 1989)	Residents are more aware of their surroundings and are better able to mobilize safely.
3. Role of all support services is enhanced by involvement in interdisciplinary conference and nursing management meetings.	Involvement of staff from all departments is necessary to obtain their input, keep them up-to-date and gain their support.	Continuity of attitudes and care.
4. An educational module was developed for the Nursing Care Plan Process.[1]	The care plan guides the staff in the individual application of Gentlecare[1] concepts.	Consistency of care across all levels of staff.
5. Activity Programs were adjusted to focus on special programs and integrate residents into facility programs as individual potential allowed.	"The residents reduced personal space can be made rich in opportunities and challenges."[2]	"Meaningful activity that is repetitive and within the residents' capability increases self-esteem and fellowship."[2]
6. A Bath Program was developed to provide residents with a comfortable and enjoyable experience.[1]	"Bathing is an intimate activity, it is difficult to accept help from anyone, especially strangers."[2]	"Problem behaviours associated with bathing are avoided when one regular staff member is in charge."[2]

Moyra Jones Resources
Video "Love is Not Enough"

STANDARD V   CARE PROGRAM cont'd

COMPOSITION OF COMMITTEE: Interdisciplinary, to include Administration, Registered Nurses, Health Care Workers and Paramedical Staff.

PURPOSE OF COMMITTEE: To review individual needs, develop plan of care and special programs to meet those needs.

DECISION	RATIONALE	EFFECT
7. Patio Program was developed.	"Walking is good exercise and therapy, nature is uplifting and fresh air is . . . exhilarating." (Gwyther 1985)	Fresh air, gentle exercise and laughter, combined with the special supportive care redirects resident's energy.
8. The Bowel Program was based on fibre, fluids and daily monitoring. Designated nursing actions as well as education programs for staff and forms for documenting results were included.	"Taking care of one's own toileting needs is fundamental to personal dignity and control."[2]	Residents have regular bowel habits using nonintrusive and natural methods.
9. Family support meetings are held six times a year.	"Quiet time, conversation and time with families creates contentment."[2]	Families understand and participate in the care and needs of their loved ones.
10. The Volunteer Program was reviewed and revised.	Volunteers are effective in providing relaxation and companionship.	Effective volunteer support.

Moyra Jones Resources
Video "Love is Not Enough"

STANDARD VI QUALITY ASSURANCE

COMPOSITION OF COMMITTEE: Interdisciplinary, to include Administration, Registered Nurses, Health Care Workers and Support Staff.

PURPOSE OF COMMITTEE: To develop an orientation and education program meeting the specific needs of the Special Care Unit.

DECISION	RATIONALE	EFFECT
1. Needs assessment using questionnaires and discussions.	Staff feel involved in and committed to the program. They receive the specific information they require.	Encourages the application of new knowledge, attitudes and skills.
2. A certificate program was designed for all employees entitled Gentlecare[1] for Progressive Degenerating Dementia. Eight sessions of 30 minutes each are provided inhouse.	Demonstrated administrative support and familiarity with the application of Gentlecare[1] concepts requires dramatic changes in attitudes and skills of all the staff.	Support, reassurance and praise are the basis of the Gentlecare[1] concept.

Moyra Jones Resources
Video "Love is Not Enough"

STANDARD VII QUALITY ASSURANCE

COMPOSITION OF COMMITTEE: Interdisciplinary to include Administration, Registered Nurses, Health Care Workers, and Paramedical Staff.

PURPOSE OF COMMITTEE: To establish Quality Assurance plans and activities.

DECISION	RATIONALE	EFFECT
1. Criteria for admission to the Special Care Unit was developed.	To assure appropriate admissions to the unit.	The unit has residents that benefit from the programs.
2. Special Care Unit Interdisciplinary Team Conferences are held on admission, after six weeks and every six months.	Individualize and update care plans as ability changes.	Current care plans are effective.
3. Special Care Unit Goals and Objectives, Policies and Procedures and Programs are reviewed and revised annually.	As programs develop and new insights occur, reviews are required.	Programs keep up with current needs and knowledge.
4. Special Care Unit audits are conducted monthly and action plans formed.	The effectiveness of resident care programs must be documented.	Successful aspects can be improved and problem areas identified and remedied.

Moyra Jones Resources
Video "Love is Not Enough"

The Handbook for Residents

The Oak Bay Kiwanis Pavilion is truly a home. It is not unusual to find a dog or a cat that belongs to the professional staff making rounds to visit people. The visits are carefully controlled and monitored but those used to having man's best friend around the house really enjoy the visits of furry friends. As in all homes, the rules are few, comfort is encouraged and activities are planned by you and for you.

The *Handbook* developed by the staff is a good example of the information that should be available for the asking.

References

English, R.A. (1989) Implementing a Nonrestraint Philosophy. P. 120 *Canadian Nurse*. March

Gwyther, L.P. (1985) Care of Alzheimer's Patients: A Manual for Nursing Home Staff. *American Health Care Association & Alzheimer Disease and Related Disorders.*

OAK BAY KIWANIS PAVILION
3034 Cedar Hill Road, Victoria, B.C. V8T 3J2
Telephone (604) 598-2022

HANDBOOK

WELCOME TO OAK BAY KIWANIS PAVILION

The members of the Board of the Oak Bay Kiwanis Health Care Society and the staff of the Oak Bay Kiwanis Pavilion take great pride and pleasure in welcoming you to our beautiful Intermediate Care Facility.

This facility is the result of the vision and dedication of Oak Bay Kiwanians, whose dreams were realized with the official opening on May 14, 1982. The six million dollar capital funding was provided by the Federal Government through the Canada Mortgage and Housing Corporation, and the year-by-year operational budget is covered through funding provided by the British Columbia Ministry of Health.

We are certain you will have some questions about our facility and it is with this in mind that we list here some of the most commonly asked questions and answers.

Mr. Reg Reid
President & Chairman of the Board

Q. WHAT TYPE OF ACCOMMODATION DOES THE PAVILION PROVIDE?

Our home provides accommodation for 121 residents. Each room is private and equipped with a washroom, including toilet and sink. All rooms are fully furnished, although you may also bring in personal items.

Q. WHAT ARTICLES AND PERSONAL BELONGINGS MAY A RESIDENT BRING INTO THE PAVILION?

Residents are welcome to bring in a favorite armchair, pictures, knick-knacks, walking canes or aids, and small electrical items, i.e., portable televisions (20" recommended), a radio, an alarm clock, a small record player, and an electric razor. These items must be CSA approved and are to be checked by our Maintenance Department prior to placement in the room.

Electrical items such as electric blankets, heating pads or electric kettles are not permitted. Valuable items such as jewelry, paintings, etc. are brought in at the resident's own risk and separate insurance for these items is highly recommended.

Q. MAY A RESIDENT BRING IN A PET?

A pet bird or a tropical fish tank are permitted only if the resident can be totally responsible for the cleaning required. Pavilion staff cannot be responsible for this additional work.

Q. DOES THE PAVILION PROVIDE TOILETRY ITEMS?

No. Items such as bars of soap and kleenex are not provided by the Pavilion; however, these items may easily be purchased at the residents' Tuck Shop.

Q. WHAT IS THE FEE FOR ACCOMMODATION AT THE OAK BAY KIWANIS PAVILION?

The accommodation rate per day is determined by the Ministry of Health of British Columbia. You will be notified of any rate changes as they are announced by the Ministry of Health.

Q. WHAT ARE THE MEAL TIMES?

The meal times vary according to each unit. The daily menu is posted on the menu board near each dining room. Every lunch and dinner main entree' is provided with an alternate choice.

A sign-up sheet is located adjacent to the posted menu so that anyone wishing an alternative is asked to sign up before 11:00 a.m. for lunch and 3:30 p.m. for dinner on the same day.

Q. MAY A RESIDENT BRING A GUEST TO MEAL TIMES?

Guests are welcome to join the residents for meals. A few hours notice is necessary to allow the kitchen sufficient preparation time. Exceptions to this early notification can be made if necessary. Payment for a guest's meal may be made at the front office.

Q. IS THERE A BAR SERVICE AVAILABLE TO RESIDENTS?

Yes. There is a bar located in the main floor library area; hours of operation are 3:30 to 4:30 p.m. every day except Sunday. This service is available to residents and their guests.

Q. ARE RESIDENTS ABLE TO MAKE THEMSELVES A CUP A TEA?

Yes. Two greenhouse lounges on the main floor provide centres for residents to make themselves a cup of tea or coffee throughout the day. Snacks are provided for residents three times a day.

Q. HOW MUCH MONEY SHOULD RESIDENTS KEEP ON HAND?

For the convenience of the residents, funds may be deposited in a trust account in the resident's name at the front office to allow access to spending money during the day. Money can be withdrawn between 10:00 a.m. and 12:00 p.m. and between 2:00 p.m. and 4:00 p.m., Monday through Friday. The maximum deposit allowed by the B.C. Ministry of Health, Long Term Care, is $120.00 at any time.

We cannot be responsible for valuables or money kept in the resident's room, therefore, it is recommended that only a small amount of money be kept on hand (i.e., $5.00). Every room comes equipped with one drawer that may be locked for valuables to be placed.

Q. WHAT ARE THE VISITING HOURS?

There are no restrictions on visiting hours. For security purposes, doors will be locked at 9:00 p.m. every night. Access is available through the main front entrance.

Q. IS THERE PARKING AVAILABLE FOR VISITORS?

Visitor parking is located in the main parking lot on the Cedar Hill Road side of the Pavilion only.

Q. ARE THERE GUIDELINES FOR RESIDENTS WISHING TO LEAVE THE PAVILION FOR POSSIBLE OUTINGS?

Residents can continue to enjoy outings and family functions outside the home whenever possible. We believe that it is important for residents to enjoy the change of atmosphere and the chance to keep in touch with long time friends and family.

We do ask that residents, family members or friends let the R.N. know, at least one hour before you depart. This enables everything to be ready. If residents are leaving overnight, or for several days, the nurse will need to be notified at least one day prior in order to arrange medication and cancel meals.

The B.C. Long Term Care Program allows a certain number of leave days per year.

SIGN OUT BOOK

To ensure the safety of all residents, we request that when leaving the Pavilion, the sign out book located at the Nursing Station be completed. The information required includes the resident's name and destination.

Q. ARE THERE RULES REGARDING SMOKING?

For the safety of residents and the comfort of others, our smoking regulations are strictly enforced. Smoking is allowed only in the following designated area:

Resident Library

Our Nursing Staff reserves the right to restrict smoking habits of individuals should they become a hazard to themselves or others.

Q. CAN THE RESIDENTS EXPECT FIRE DRILLS?

For the safety and protection of the residents, fire drills are held monthly. If the fire alarm rings, residents and guests must remain in their rooms. Doors will close automatically. Please close the windows if you are able. Your Nursing department will keep you informed and give you further instructions as necessary.

Q. DOES THE PAVILION HAVE A LADIES AUXILIARY?

The service of the Tuck Shop are available through the diligent efforts of the Oak Bay Kiwanis Ladies Auxiliary and are performed on a volunteer basis.

Proceeds from the Tuck Shop and bar sales provide funds for various projects for the Pavilion residents.

Q. IS CABLE TELEVISION AVAILABLE TO THE RESIDENTS?

Cable TV outlets are available in every room. The charge for this service is the responsibility of the resident.

Quiet Time: The Residents' Council issued a recommendation (1983) that all radios, stereos and televisions be turned down in volume by 10:00 p.m. nightly, to avoid annoyance to fellow residents.

Earphones, which can readily be attached to the above equipment, are available at stereo stores. Many residents living here have had this adjustment made and are satisfied with the results.

Q. CAN RESIDENTS HAVE THEIR OWN TELEPHONES?

Telephone outlets are available in each room; however, individual arrangements must be made with the telephone company for listing and installation. Telephone charges are the individual responsibility of each resident.

Q. WHAT IS THE PROCEDURE FOR RESIDENTS' PERSONAL LAUNDRY?

Laundry services are provided at no extra charge for Pavilion residents. For best results, we suggest that only "wash and wear" articles be sent to the laundry. The schedule for pick up and delivery can be obtained from the Nursing Staff.

All clothing sent to the laundry must be clearly marked in order to avoid loss. This will be done by Pavilion staff, however there will be a small charge for labels.

Clothing that is not washable and requires special handling (dry cleaning) may be left at the front office for pick up and subsequent delivery on a regular basis. Frequent articles of clothing that require dry cleaning are woolen suits, coats, jackets and dresses. Residents are responsible for payment of their own dry cleaning.

Q. IS THERE A BEAUTY SALON AND/OR BARBER SHOP?

These services are available on a regular basis. Services and prices are posted in the beauty salon.

Q. WHAT TYPE OF RECREATIONAL ACTIVITIES ARE PROVIDED FOR THE RESIDENTS?

The Activities Department offers a wide variety of recreational programs seven days a week. An Activity Calendar is posted on each unit every month, as well as residents receive individual calendars for their rooms. A resident newspaper is published each month for residents and their families. There is also a Residents' Council which meets on a monthly basis.

Some of the monthly programs include out-trips into the community, a fitness program, reading and discussion groups, social events, such as monthly birthday parties, luncheons and pub nights. Other activities include baking groups, outdoor barbeques (during the summer), garden groups and a drama club. There are also weekly church services for those residents who wish to attend.

Q. ARE THERE FAMILY NIGHTS?

Yes. Six times per year Family Nights are planned. Upon admission, family members will receive a calendar of events. Family Nights are a combination of social and recreational functions, or informational and educational presentations. We encourage family members to attend any resident function as often as they wish.

Chapter 9

REFLECTIONS

Interface

Nightmares and memories,
intertwined.
Tell me, which is yours,
which is mine?
Arthur Olson

There are many concerns, confusions and remaining questions related to Alzheimer's disease which are still unresolved. One of the most conscious concerns to me is my feeling that although I know that Aila's brain is continuing to deteriorate and that her brain no longer communicates well with her body we are nevertheless communicating. There is a feeling between us that I can't explain. It is as real as spoken speech and as warm as love.

During our journey, I came in contact with Dr. Wilder Penfield's book, *The Mystery of the Mind*. Dr. Penfield was a Canadian and, until his death in 1976, one of the world's foremost neurologists. His more than forty years of study of the brain brought him to the question: "Do brain mechanisms account for the mind? Can the mind be explained by what is now known of the brain? If not, which is the more reasonable of two hypotheses; that man's being is based on one element, or on two?"

Penfield states that we cannot say where the mind comes from but that it does exist and is related to some mechanism within the brain. The mind and the brain develop together, but apart. They develop together, feed on each other and pass through life as partners, each non-functioning without the other.

The mind conditions the brain and as the years pass it becomes stronger, freer to explore the world of thought, both its own and others. As the body becomes weak and frail with age and as the brain tires, the mind grows in its capacity for its own fulfilment because it has no inevitable pathology.

Penfield poses the question: What becomes of the mind after death of the body and the brain?

Nonetheless, since the exact nature of the mind is a mystery and the source of its energy has yet to be identified, no scientist is in a position to say that direct communication between two active minds cannot occur during life. He may say that unassailable evidence of it has not yet been brought forward.

Direct communication between the mind of man and the mind of God is quite another matter. The argument in favour of this lies in the claim made by so many men, for so long a time, that they have received guidance and revelation from some power beyond themselves through the medium of prayer. I see no reason to doubt this evidence, nor any means of submitting it to scientific proof.

Penfield goes on to say that if the mind is not to die with the brain and the body then some kind of connection must be made with an energy source other than the brain. If, however, direct communication can be made, during life, to minds of other people or God, it is possible that energies can merge. Penfield states: "In that case, it is not unreasonable for him to hope that after death the mind may waken to another source of energy."

If you were to compare mind and soul in the dictionary you would find the same definition.

In the last few years, as Aila and I have experienced Alzheimer's disease together I am convinced that just as an unconscious person, perhaps in a coma, can relate what happened around them when they awake, a person afflicted with Alzheimer's disease has a mind that is untouched by the disease. How else can you explain that toward the end of her life she seems to be in another world that has happy memories and perhaps vivid images? How else can you explain that in the middle of unintelligible speech, she reaches out and clearly says, "I love you?"

Medical experts tell us that with a person in a coma it is important to talk to them, to communicate through all the senses. Why is it less important with the Alzheimer's patient? Every day that I visit Aila, I talk to her, telling her what I'm doing, what the children are doing, how the weather is outside and sometimes something that happened that is humorous. It is amazing what a difference laughter makes.

One of the nurses told me that it is not unusual to find that Alzheimer's patients, near the end of their lives, will be anxious and fighting to stay alive until someone they love tells them that it is okay to let go, that they love them and they will be all right. Doesn't that give you pause to think that perhaps there is more to death than you thought? I tried this with Aila, telling her that it was okay to let go. I think it made a difference. She is calmer and more at peace with the shrinking world that her physical body experiences. As Edna St. Vincent Millay expressed in one of her poems, of which I have forgotten the name, "over these things I cannot see for these are the things that bounded me."

Consent

I wait for death,
Not mine but Aila's.
How strange to wait for the death of another.
It puts a period on the sentence of life.
The very concept means acceptance,
and yet acceptance means consent.
Have I agreed to let her die?

I wait for death.
By what right have I agreed to see it come?
Come it will, but must I consent?
Can I not reach out and hold her,
perhaps to keep it at a distance,
to disperse its power with my presence.

I am indeed a fool to believe
that I can stay the last pinpoint of ink upon the page.
An accident of motion could make the pinpoint drop,
finish without consent the final line.
                    Arthur Olson

The ward is quiet except for the now-less-frequent burst of vocal energy from Bob as he paces the corridor looking for an unknown friend or place to rest. Some new friends have appeared and others gone on another journey, having passed into that dark night. Rosa still cares for Aila by patting and rearranging her leg blanket, combing her hair and making the sign of the cross on her forehead. Aila doesn't mind her intrusion any more and seems to accept the attention as a natural occurrence in the day's events. Sometimes she even responds to the attention and calls her Mother. Rosa leaves with a "God be praised" or "Glory to God" only to return in a few minutes to renew the ritual now so quickly forgotten.

John, in his track suit, trots down the hall, his body bent against an unseen wind of gale force. I once asked Irene why John ran. "John was in another nursing home before he came to us," she said. "They kept him in restraints so that he wouldn't wander or run." No wonder the man wanted to be free. It was a means of expressing his independence and individuality as a human being.

Over the last year and a half that Aila has been in the Oak Bay Kiwanis Pavilion, in my amateur capacity as a people watcher, I have been amazed at the tenaciousness of the Alzheimer's disease victims who hold to their dignity, personality and individual being. They never become vegetables. The ability to retain quirks of personality, a characteristic expression, movement or smile, remain and are cherished by us. The soul (mind) of each becomes more visible as the brain deteriorates and it is a marvel to behold. How wise our creator must be.

As time passes and the patients' names on the doors change, I can't help but think of the song line "and nobody knows my name." The caregivers know, but the patients are unaware that a momentary friend from across the hall or the next room is no longer there. At first, I thought: How weird, how unnatural, how unkind. I must be visiting another world or planet where the frame of reference is beyond my comprehension. But then I thought: I'm looking at this process from a weird point of view myself. How cruel it would be for Aila to see the names changing, to be aware of the significance, to know that the name tag on her door would soon change. Being unaware of the surroundings and the significance of change no longer creates the depression I used to feel on hearing, "and nobody knows my name."

Alzheimer's disease is terrible to experience, as a victim or an observer. In its early stages, it is frightening and incomprehensible. In the final stages it is devastating and debilitating. Human nature, however, is heroic, monumental and courageous. We have a great capacity to laugh and cry at the same time. Cry for the anticipation but laugh at the joy of a moment between the tears.

Aila doesn't cry any more but she does laugh. Oh, what a great laugh she has. I can't help but laugh with her, often at the unknown for me but not for her. I think that perhaps she knows something I don't and is teasing me as she did in earlier days.

At the time of this writing, Aila can no longer use her wheelchair because she lacks the strength. Her recliner is her world; her memories are of her childhood companions. We sit, holding hands and wait between the tears and laughter.

November 1991. This month marks the second anniversary of when Aila entered the Oak Bay Kiwanis Pavilion. We have both learned the terms and survival techniques of living apart: Aila, unaware of her surroundings, and I drawn deeper and deeper with each passing day into the horror of watching not only Aila dying from the disease, but also others who have become part of my life.

Watching each patient, over the years, become more detached from this world and seeing the physical changes that occur daily makes those of us who visit our loved ones each day develop a camaraderie. We seldom ask, "How is ____ ?" but rather, "How are you?" We have seen one another cry. We know of the pain that exists through our understanding of the end. We have seen each other caring, not only for our own, but for others. The association creates within each one of us an appreciation and affection for those we know in this place of sickness. We also know that the communal understanding and appreciation will be gone when our loved one dies. The sorrow and pain will not want to be remembered. If we meet on the street, we know that no questions beyond, "How are you doing, are you well?" will be asked. No question about the well-being of their loved ones because we know the answer before it is asked. We have developed a new code of communication so as not to stir up near-surface emotion.

The once unfamiliar routine of the nursing home has become familiar. I can look at the board to see who is taking care of Aila during the work shifts, what day she will have her turn in the whirlpool bath and what will be the menu for each of the meals. I know the sounds of the hall and dining room and what they mean.

Bob has gone. The verbal outbursts no longer echo down the hall, and the occasional "shut up" heard from someone disturbed has ceased. It became obvious to us all that something was missing, an irritant was gone. And yet, how strange — we missed him. You could count on Bob to make you listen. You could count on him to elicit a response from others. You could count on him for the occasional "What a guy!" that made us laugh. We miss him but we are glad that he is free.

May broke her arm and sits in isolated confusion cradling her cast like a young mother would a child. She feels the pain and will not eat or drink, yet she smiles. Perhaps she knows instinctively, as so many do, that not getting well is a way to be free.

Aila still keeps us guessing. I always think back to one day, years ago, when she said, "Aren't you glad I married you?

Think of what a dull life you would have had. You would probably have married another teacher, had kids who never made mistakes and would never have known life." You know, she was right. I wouldn't want to have missed a day. Life is to be lived not merely got through.

Over the past two years, Aila has progressed from the middle stages of the disease to the final stage. There have been incidents that particularly stand out in my mind as being benchmarks of the deteriorating aspects of the disease. Many images are blurred. The symptoms of the disease seemed to accelerate after Aila went into the nursing home with plateaus where no change occurred — and then the rapid slide. It seems to me that for a long period of time I would greet her as she was walking down the hall with her back straight and her stride purposeful. The horror of getting off the elevator one day and seeing her coming down the hall, her back bent, holding the railing for balance, was only the beginning of what was to come.

It all seemed to happen so rapidly. It was no more than a week after her balance was gone that she was in a wheelchair, no longer able to explore her limited environment. Her knee joints lost their flexibility and she was going blind. Her ability to communicate, even limitedly, disappeared and was replaced by the occasional "yes" or "no" that was usually not related to any external content or question. Her ability to smile was lost. That beautiful smile that said my Aila was still there within that frail body was gone.

There are also other images that make me smile and appreciate the kindness of the care helpers who take care of Aila. One day early in May, when I got off the elevator, Shannon told me that Aila was out on the patio and to go out and enjoy lunch with her. Aila was sitting in her wheelchair, in her best dress and matching sun-hat, among the flowers at one of the patio tables, shaded by a large umbrella. The table was set for two with napkins, wine glasses and a vase of roses. We were served salad, soup and a main dish (I can't remember what it was now). I remember the thoughtfulness of the staff in doing this for us and the parting comment, "Just sit and enjoy the afternoon, kids." It is a visual memory I will always cherish.

As I write this final chapter of our life together, Aila is dying. Her chest is gradually becoming more congested and soon her lungs will cease to function. The children and I discussed what medical intervention we will want when the situation arises where a decision has to be made. I know Aila's feelings from earlier discussions and we agreed on no medical intervention. Aila will receive no antibiotics, no intravenous feeding and no resuscitation should her heart fail. With the aid of morphine, she will "go gentle into that good night."

The death certificate will read respiratory failure but it should read Alzheimer's disease. For all the Ailas and Bobs in this world we need to find the cause and a cure for this terrible disease.

Gently My Love

Go freely, gently, my love,
Don't wait for me,
Run free through your field,
Laughing, your hair flying in the wind.

Sit on your rock by the lake,
Row for your grandfather — fishing,
"The best rower he ever had," he said.
Sleep in your grandmother's bed when
you're afraid of the storm.

Stretch your arms and legs in luxury,
Pick the flowers and ride Rex on the wind,
Look your fill into the sky,
Reach up your hands and scream to feel them
touch the clouds,
You are free.

Arthur Olson

Chapter 10

TWO ARTICLES ON RESEARCH
IN ALZHEIMER'S DISEASE

The two articles that make up this chapter provide in-depth information for those who wish more clinical, scientific information concerning Alzheimer's disease. Both of the articles are written for geriatric specialists but they can be easily understood by anyone who has had contact with the disease. I found that they gave me background which enabled me to talk intelligently with specialists, and gave me some valuable insights that I would have found difficult to acquire in any other way.

Acute decompensation in dementia: Recognition and management

C. PATTERSON, MD   J. K. Le CLAIR, MD

Dementing illnesses are chronic disorders causing global impairment of intellectual function. The most common cause is Alzheimer's disease, and this, together with most other forms of dementing ilness, is relentlessly progressive. Frequently, however, there is an abrupt deterioration in physical, behavioral, or cognitive function in someone who is known to suffer from a dementing illness. This article outlines an approach to the many factors capable of producing such acute decompensation.

Patterson C, Le Clair JK. Acute decompensation in dementia: Recognition and management. Geriatrics 1989; 44 (Aug): 20-32.

Rapid deterioration occurring over a period of hours, weeks, or months in a patient with a dementing illness such as Alzheimer's disease may signal the presence of a superimposed physical, psychiatric, or social problem. These acute or subacute decompensations are often treatable, and must be distinguished from the natural course of the primary dementing condition (see Natural history of dementia, p. 21). Effective interventions and appropriate therapy can result in improved quality of life for the patient and caregiver.

This article reviews potential causes of acute decompensation which may be physical, psychiatric, environmental, a natural progression

Dr. Patterson is associate professor and head, Division of Geriatric Medicine, Department of Medicine, McMaster University, Hamilton, Ontario. Dr. Le Clair is assistant professor and deputy head, Division of Geriatric Psychiatry, Department of Psychiatry, McMaster University, Hamilton, Ontario.

of the disease, or a combination of these factors (table 1). Unraveling and prioritizing the causes for decompensation can be accomplished using the method discussed in this review (summarized in figure 1).

Physical factors

Physical or "medical" causes of acute decompensation usually lead to a delirium superimposed on the dementing illness. The hallmark of a delirium is a clouding of consciousness, which may arise from a wide variety of causes.[4] Other features of delirium include perceptual disturbance such as hallucinations, disturbances of speech (usually slurring or incoherence) and a disturbance or reversal of the sleep-wake cycle. Memory is affected globally.

More subtle impairment of consciousness level may be manifested by inattention, loss of concentration, or a variable sense of orientation. Activity may either be heightened or reduced and drowsiness may be evident. The course of a delirium characteristically fluctuates, with an acute or subacute onset which may clear days or even weeks after the specific etiology is remedied. The psychiatric manual DSM-IIIR lists several prominent features of delirium (table 2).

The acronym D.E.M.E.N.T.I.A. (table 3) may be useful in remembering typical causes of delirium. This is not meant to imply, of course, that delirium and dementia are synonymous. The potential causes are arranged as an acronym but not in order of prevalence. Infection would be placed much higher, for example, if the list were prioritized. Nonetheless, this acronym can serve as a useful memory aid.

Drugs. Drugs commonly implicated include anticholinergic drugs of all types (table 4). These drugs induce a worsening of confusion in the demented patient, as dementias, particularly that of the Alzheimer's type, are associated with impaired cholinergic neural transmission, and the additional insult of an anticholinergic drug may cause severe neurotransmitter disturbance.

Drug withdrawal, particularly from barbiturates, benzodiazepines, and alcohol, may result in a delirium which may be hyperactive and have hallucinations as a prominent feature. Miscellaneous drugs such as dioxin, cimetidine, NSAIDs, and antihypertensives may also produce delirium.[5]

Endocrine disturbances. Endocrine disturbances may impair consciousness and lead to delirium. Common examples include hypoglycemia and hypercalcemia. More rarely, myxedema and disturbances of cortisol secretion, such as Cushing's disease and Addison's disease, may lead to delirium.

Metabolic disturbances. The most common metabolic reasons for delirium include organ failure such as respiratory failure, cardiac failure, hepatic failure, and dehydration.

Malnutrition may also result in delirium, as a demented person may not eat properly. Thus, nutritional deficiencies, particularly of thiamin and vitamin B12, should be considered.

Epileptic seizures. Epileptic seizures occur increasingly commonly with advancing age. These seizures may be the result of pre-existing brain damage, such as stroke, or they may occur spontaneously in degenerative brain conditions, such as Alzheimer's disease.

The seizure may be atypical, ie, convulsive movements may be absent (akinetic seizure), or unwitnessed, with postictal confusion the only clue to the recent seizure.

Seizures may, of course, be induced by metabolic conditions such as hyponatremia and hypocalcemia. They may also occur in the setting of cardiac asystole or serious arrhythmia.

Neoplasms. Neoplasms may cause delirium either by direct mass effects due to tumor or cerebral edema, or by their remote effects. The remote effects of tumor may include endocrine abnormalities such as hypercalcemia or syndrome of inappropriate ADH secretion (SIADH).

Other remote non-metastatic effects of carcinoma include limbic encephalopathy and multifocal leukoencephalopathy.

Trauma. Trauma may cause delirium, either by concussion or by the development of subdural hematoma. Trauma that is remote from the central nervous system may also cause delirium. For example, a demented person who develops a fracture of a major bone such as the hip may be unable to localize or describe the pain, and may simply present with worsened confusion. Delirium that occurs postoperatively is due to the trauma of surgery itself and the frequent drug and metabolic effects which accompany it.

NATURAL HISTORY OF DEMENTIA

Dementia is best described as a syndrome of global cognitive impairment, without depression of the level of consciousness. The diagnostic and statistical manual of the American Psychiatric Association (DSM-IIIR) includes in its definition of dementia a degree of intellectual impairment sufficient to impair occupational or social functioning.[1]

In the older person who suffers from dementia, the most common cause is Alzheimer's disease.[2] This begins insidiously and the exact time of onset of symptoms can rarely be ascertained. Usually the illness unfolds in a gradually progressive, indolent manner, often reaching clinical expression as a result of memory loss. This may lead to forgetting appointments, failure to recognize members of the family, leaving pots on the stove, or becoming lost in familiar surroundings. Alternatively, the illness may present with a change in personality, mood, or in behavior such as the commencement of wandering, agressiveness, or uninhibited actions.

Gradually, over a period of years, language, praxis, continence, and physical function may be affected, with death characteristically occurring within 5 to 10 years of onset of the illness.[3]

Dementia may also accompany other neurological diseases, particularly Parkinson's disease, Huntington's disease, and progressive supranuclear palsy. Under these circumstances the neurological disease is usually prominent, although the dementia may have preceded the neurological signs. Dementia may also be the result of chronic chemical intoxication with alcohol or repeated head trauma (eg. dementia pugilistica).

Although most cases of dementia are not due to cerebral vascular disease, multiple strokes may lead to a multi-infarct dementia. Here, the history is characteristically different, with discrete neurological events occurring over a period of months or years. Under these circumstances the onset of dementia may be abrupt and the course a "step-wise" deterioration.

Regardless of the cause of dementia, the degree of intellectual impairment may remain relatively stable for prolonged periods of time.

C. PATTERSON, MD.
J.K. LeCLAIR, MD.

Infections. Infections are a very common cause of delirium. They may cause confusion, either by their effects on organ function (eg, pneumonia causing respiratory failure) or for less readily explained reasons. Examples include the confusion that so often accompanies urinary tract infection or, less commonly, intra-abdominal or biliary tract infections. The possibility of meningitis or encephalitis, whose signs may be subtle or even absent in an elderly demented person, should not be overlooked. Remember that infection in the frail demented elderly may present without the usual fever and leukocytosis that occurs in a younger person.

Apoplexy. Vascular events – labeled here for our purposes by the admittedly anachronistic "apoplexy" – may trigger decompensation in dementia. This decompensation may be the result of a stroke, resulting in a further loss of functioning cerebral tissue, or of a vascular event affecting another system. Common examples include myocardial infarction, pulmonary embolism, and peripheral or abdominal embolism. Tissue necrosis due to gangrene is also often associated with delirium.

Remember that a relatively small insult, such as upper respiratory infection, minor drug overdoses, or small changes in electrolyte balance, may lead to a worsening of confusion in a previously demented person.

Very commonly, delirium in debilitated elderly patients has several causes operating at once. This situation is sometimes referred to as the "bits", ie. deterioration may be due to a "bit of" infection, a "bit of" electrolyte disturbance, and so on.

Psychiatric factors

In general, the acute decompensations

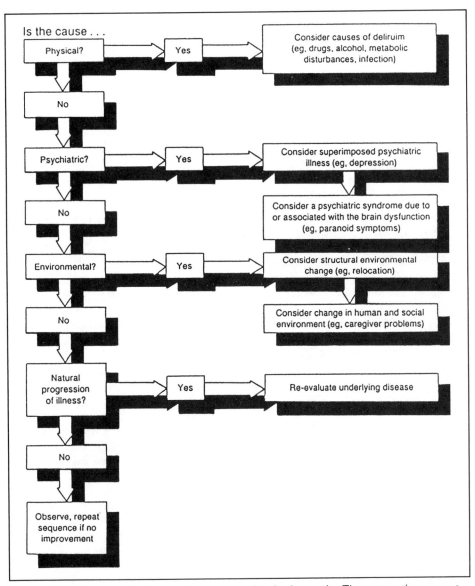

Figure. Decision tree for acute decompensation in dementia. The categories are not mutually exclusive and interaction of factors must be considered.

Courtesy of the authors

TABLE 1

CAUSES OF ACUTE DECOMPENSATION IN DEMENTIA

Physical	– Delirium (for causes see table 3)
Psychiatric	– Co-existing major psychiatric disorder – Psychiatric syndrome or symptom due to underlying brain disorder – Catastrophic reaction
Environmental	– Change in caregivers – Change in physical environment – Relocation to hospital or institution
Natural progression	– Stroke – Jakob-Creutzfeld disease – Progressive Alzheimer's disease (rarely acute)

Source: Prepared for GERIATRICS by the authors

due to psychiatric reasons present more gradually than other types; rather than the hours or days seen with superimposed medical problems, psychiatric-induced decompensation is often described in terms of weeks or months.

It is nevertheless imperative to consider possible medical triggers when faced with a recent onset of psychiatric or behavioral problems in the demented, no matter what the symptom complex or time course of onset. Once medical triggers have been ruled out, several psychiatric reasons for decompensation should then be considered. Admittedly, ruling in a superimposed psychiatric illness is difficult and time consuming, but since these conditions are highly treatable, the effort can be rewarding. It is certain that if these conditions are missed or ignored, they will impact negatively, and unnecessarily so, on quality of life for both the patient and the caregiver.

Co-existent major psychiatric illness. The demented patient who decompensates emotionally, behaviorally, or cognitively and who has historically shown a vulnerability to

major psychiatric disorder should be suspected of having a reoccurrence of that disorder as a reason for decompensation.

This is particularly important in the elderly because psychiatric disorders such as depression have a tendency towards increased rates of recidivism and pervasiveness in old age. While depression (particularly bipolar disorders) in the non-demented elderly occurs at higher rates with shorter illness-free periods than in the younger population, the demented patient's vulnerability to re-expression may be further enhance by the inherent stresses associated with his or her cognitive decline.

Suspicion of a major psychiatric decline should be enhanced by a positive family history or previous psychiatric illness discovered through careful inquiry. Often this history is not readily available, since the patient and the caregivers fail to recall, or at times actually conceal, such problems. Careful questioning of many individuals who have known the patient is therefore essential in these cases.

The clinician should explore for any history merely suggestive of a previous psychiatric illness; today's elderly cohort often did not seek treatment or were misdiagnosed in the past. A history of a disorder characterized by withdrawal, dysphoria, and anhedonia, lasting several months and recovering spontaneously, but which was historically ascribed to a viral disorder, may have actually been an undiagnosed primary affective disorder. The clinician should also seek out new symptoms that may suggest depression, such as unusual behaviors or apparently stressful reactions to recent adverse events in the patient's life.

In contrast to the apathy seen in dementia, depression will often be characterized by mood disturbances. Extreme withdrawal, refusal to eat, or histrionic, inconsistent behavior can be signs of depression as well as the more typical hopelessness, suicidal ideation, and significant problems with self-esteem. Other indicators of major psychiatric disorder include feelings of intense guilt, negative ruminations and distortions of the past, delusions of poverty, and paranoia.

Exploration of recent history and use of a mental status examination can further sensitize one to the presence of major psychiatric problems. The test should include a quantifiable test score, such as the Folstein Mini-Mental Status Examination,[6] which can be repeated to assess progress or decline.

Neurological basis. Superimposed psychiatric decline in dementia may be cause by the neurological disorder itself. Growing evidence supports the view that psychiatric disorders or symptoms may occur in dementia as a result of the brain dysfunction.[7] CNS dysregulation associated with strokes, Alzheimer's disease, and other neurological conditions is deemed, under this hypothesis, to be uncovering or producing major psychiatric sequelae.

Left frontal infarcts have been associated with increased occurrences of depressive syndromes at a much higher rate that insults occurring elsewhere in the brain.[8] Increased depression has been noted in Parkinson's disease more frequently than in other illnesses of a similar debilitating nature.[9] Late onset manic disorders have been found in elderly males with neurological lesions,[10] and depressive disorder in Huntington's is well recognized.

All of these neurologic-related

TABLE 2

CLINICAL FEATURES OF DELIRIUM (modified from DSM-IIIR)

Clouding of consciousness

Abnormalities of one or more:
  Perception (eg, hallucinations)
  Speech
  Sleep/wake cycle
  Activity (increased or decreased)

Disorientation and memory disturbance

Acute or subacute onset

Fluctuating course

Specific etiology usually present

Source: Adapted from DSM-IIIR

TABLE 3

POTENTIAL CAUSES OF DELIRIUM: CHECKLIST

D Drugs

E Endocrine disturbances

M Metabolic disturbances

E Epilepsy and seizure disorder

N Neoplasm

T Trauma

I Infection

A "Apoplexy" or vascular event

TABLE 4

SELECTED ANTICHOLINERGIC DRUGS THAT MAY CAUSE DELIRIUM, AND SUGGESTED ALTERNATIVES

Pharmacological type	Examples	Alternatives
Antiparkinsonian agents	Benztrophine Trihexyphenidyl	L-dopa compounds
Antihistamines	Diphenhydramine	
Antiemetics	Dimenhydrinate	Metoclopramide
Opthalmic drugs	Atropine	
Tricyclic	Amitriptyline	Desipramine Nortriptyline
Antiarrhythmics	Disopyramide	Quinidine Amiodarone
Antispasmodics	Propantheline	
Anesthetic agents	Atropine	

Source: Prepared for GERIATRICS by the authors

TABLE 5

CAREGIVER ASSESSMENT CONSIDERATIONS

Physical and psychiatric health of the caregiver

Premorbid relationship of the caregiver and patient

Support for the caregiver

Behaviour of the patient, caregiver understanding, interaction and impact

Source: Prepared for GERIATRICS by the authors

depressive syndromes have been shown to be medically responsive to various antidepressant drug therapies.

Delusions. Thought content distortions are common in those suffering from dementias and may result in decline. In several studies symptoms such as paranoid delusions have been reported in as many as 30% of patients or more.[7] These delusions usually involve themes of stealing and are not elaborate in content. This kind of delusion is most likely seen in senile dementia of the Alzheimer's type.

In contrast, bizarre, well systematized delusions associated with hallucinatory behavior may also occur as a result of the organic problem or due to a superimposed schizophrenic disorder. For example, in Parkinson's disease, paranoid hallucinatory syndromes, are well recognized. These may be due to dopaminergic medications, but at times appear spontaneously.[11]

A "Capgras" syndrome, in which the patient believes his or her spouse is an imposter, may also present in the demented. A similar thought content distortion may occur with the demented person failing to recognize his own home, and continually asking to return to his "own home".

These ideations may go undetected, resulting in agitation, aggressive behavior towards the caregiver, and mood disturbances. If these problems are identified they can be effectively treated and previous function restored.

Environmental factors

The natural deterioration of cognitive capabilities seen in dementia may first present as a precipitous decline due to a catastrophic reaction, characterized by aggression or obvious psychiatric disturbances. The patient becomes overwhelmed, agitated, frustrated, and disorganized, and becomes rapidly dysfunctional. In these cases, reassessment of the "patient-environment fit" is essential.

The demented person is best managed within a routine and a physical environment that allows little opportunity for unexpected change. Therefore, environmental disruptions commonly lead to worsening of orientation and disturbed behavior in the demented person. For example, major disorientation may occur if the patient's spouse, to whom the patient has been strongly attached, is temporarily replaced by a home care nurse or health aid.

Similarly, taking a demented person on a journey or even changing the furniture may lead to greater disorientation. Relocation to a new institution is always a disruptive process for the cognitively impaired, though this can be minimized by having the patient take familiar articles along. Admission to a hospital with its totally alien environment is frequently a cause of severe disorientation, and may have hazardous consequences, such as falls.

Loss of autonomy, independence, memory, and other cognitive capabilities, as well as changing social relationships, lead to major adjustments for the patient and his surrounding caregiving environment. Grief, fear of death, loss of independence, and changing roles in life are but a few of the major areas of concern. Difficult though it may be, assessing and determining the major adjustments

TABLE 6

LABORATORY INVESTIGATIONS FOR WORKUP OF DELIRIUM

Usually performed

CBC
Urea
Creatinine
Electrolytes
Blood sugar
Serum calcium
Urine analysis
Chest x-ray
EKG

Additional procedures

Lumber puncture
EEG
CTT scan
Blod cultures
Drug levels

Source: Prepared for GERIATRICS by the authors

and the emotional problem and fears of the patient may point to reasons for decline and highlight avenues of appropriate intervention.

Referral to a mental health expert is advisable when a major psychiatric issue is suspected but is difficult to confirm or when management becomes complicated. Close liaison between internist and psychiatrist or psychologist is invaluable.

The crucial caregiver

The patient's caregiver may be a decisive factor determining whether the patient is able to remain at home or, at least, function well in an institution. Very often, therefore, the patient's decompensation is nothing other than a reflection of caregiver's personal difficulties.

Several important factors that the clinician should look for when assessing those caring for the demented are outlined in table 5. Consideration should be given to the mental and physical health of the caregiver. Many of those caring for the demented become depressed. This is not surprising since the caregiver must deal with the loss and consequent grief associated with the decline in the patient, the strain associated with changes in the demented person's behavior, and the entrapment which may occur as a result of the caring process.[12]

Caregivers are often elderly individuals themselves and age-related medical problems and changes in their functional capabilities have a profound effect on the delicate caregiver/patient interaction. Often however, the problem brought to the clinician is not the caregiver's impaired health but decompensation in the demented patient. Through careful inquiry, for example, a significant sleep disturbance in the caregiver may be identified. In this case, management of the demented patient's decompensation actually involves assessment and treatment of the sleep disturbance in the caregiver.

Sometimes a spouses or adult child's ineffectiveness in caring for the patient indicates a deeper problem in the relationship or family situation. Perhaps the caregiver's own family support situation is lacking. Anything that can be done to help the caregiver deal with these factors will, in effect, be the treatment of choice.

As a final caregiver issue, often the demented individual will appear physically normal, not obviously intellectually impaired, yet behave inappropriately due to the incapabili-
ties or disinhibitions arising from the dementia. It is not uncommon for the caregiver to misinterpret this behavior. Exploring the caregiver's understanding of this situation and helping him or her to deal with it will often result in improved function in the patient.[13]

Decompensation as disease progression

Even though one should always seek causes other than natural progression to explain an acute deterioration in dementia, sometimes the decompensation may in fact be due to disease progression. Acute deterioration in Alzheimer's disease is unusual, but other dementias can more commonly have a rapid course. For example, Jakob-Creutzfeld disease frequently runs its course in less than a year and may be suspected when myoclonus and seizures are prominent early on in the disease. The electroencephalogram (EEG) is usually diagnostic.

The type of dementia which characteristically deteriorates most abruptly is that due to multiple infarctions. In this case there are usually multiple risk factors for stroke, such as s hypertension, and there is usually a characteristic episodic or stuttering history.[14] Focal neurological symptoms and signs are often but not invariably present. Infarctions of the right temporal or parietal lobe can present as abrupt deterioration and delirium-like states, with no obvious neurological signs.

The progress of dementia secondary to malignant disease is also usually rapid.

A clinical approach

Recognition of the above causative factors indicates the appropriate clinical approach.

Risk assessment. The first priority, when faced with a decline in a demented individual, is to assess the degree of the patient's risk. Is the patient safe in his or her present situation and can he or she be managed appropriately under the given circumstances? High-risk situations include wandering outside, falling, and dangerous use of stoves and fires. Assessment of the degree of imminent physical danger, suicidal risk, and risk to others is imperative, and will determine the degree, type, and acuity of interventions required. The physician must be familiar with the local medical/legal system in order to assess such issues as competence, guardianship, and assignment of power of attorney.

History. Specific inquiry should be made concerning the onset of deterioration, as well as the history of the dementing process. Changes in medications, symptoms suggesting systemic disease, changes of environment, and new psychiatric symptoms are just a few of the items that should be carefully sought.

Other features of the medical history may give valuable clues to the possible reasons for decline, such as a history of congestive heart failure, recurrent infections, or depression or depression-like syndromes. Exploration of the premorbid and present relationships of the patient and caregiver can provide clues to the disturbing factors. Finally, a mental status examination should be administered.

Physical examination. The vital signs to be recorded should include temperature (taken by rectum if the oral temperature is normal). Neurological examination should include the presence of nuchal rigidity, papilledema, and focal neurological signs.

In addition, three characteristic motor abnormalities may be seen in delirium:

- Asterixis, the coarse flapping tremor that is typical of hepatic or renal failure, may also occur in various types of delirium.

- Multifocal myoclonus, ie, spontaneous contractions of isolated muscle groups, is often seen in a serious delirium.

- The phenomenon of "picking"; the patient appears to be picking things out of the air or picking up imaginary objects from the bedclothes. This results from the visual hallucinosis that often accompanies delirium.

It is essential to accurately determine and record the level of consciousness. Drowsiness and obtundation are obvious. More subtle changes in the level of consciousness may often be detected by using specific tests for attention (eg, backward counting, serial 7 subtractions). A useful clue is when the history is inconsistent. When the same question is asked at different times during the examination, the patient may lose track during a sentence, and may exhibit slurred speech.

It is often necessary to carry out some routine laboratory investigations. The decision to do so must rest upon numerous factors, including how long the problem has been present, whether there are any items in the history that may point to a specific disorder, and the location of the patient. Table 6 lists a modest laboratory workup that will identify the majority of important medical causes for delirium when taken in conjunction with history and examination.

Conclusion

Decompensation in dementia challenges the ability of all clinicians to unravel the puzzle by looking at medical, psychiatric, and social factors that may be impinging singly or in combination upon the patient. Decompensation must be distinguished from the natural course of illness, since effective interventions can lead to improved quality of life for both the demented patient and the caregiver. Assessment and management must include a thorough re-examination of all the possible determinants of rapid deterioration in a demented older patient. Failure to identify the reason for decompensation or initiation of inappropriate management may accelerate the patient's decline.

Dr. Patterson and LeClair are supported in part by the Educational Centre for Aging and Health, McMasters University.

References

1. American Psychiatric Association. Diagnostic and statistical manual disorders. Fourth ed. (DSM-IIIR) Washington, D.C. 1980.
2. Katzman R. Alzheimer's disease. N Engl J Med 1986; 314:964-973.
3. Schoenberg BS, Okazaki H, Kokmen E. Reduced survival in patients with dementia. A population study. Trans Am Neurol Assoc. 1981; 306-308.
4. Lipowski ZJ. Delirium (acute confusional states) JAMA 1987; 258:1789-1792.
5. Larson EB, Kukell WA, uchner D, Reifler BV. Adverse drug reactions associated with global cognitive impairment in elderly persons. Ann Intern Med. 1987; 107:169-173.
6. Folstein MF, Folstein SE, McHugh PR. Mini mental state: A practical method for grading the cognitive state of patients for the clinician. J Psychiatry Res. 1975; 12:189-198.
7. Merriam AE, Aranoon MK. Gaston P. Way S. Katy I. The psychiatric symptoms of Alzheimer's disease. J AM Geriatr Soc. 1988; 36:7-12.
8. Robinson RG. Starr LB. Price JR. A two year longiudinal study of mood disorder following stroke prevalence and duration at six month follow up. Br. J. Psychiatry 1984; 144:251-262.
9. Horn, S. Some psychological factors in Parkinsons. J. Neurol Neurosurg Psychiatry 1974; 37:27-31.
10. Shulman K. Post F. Bipolar affective disorder in old age. Br. J. Psychiatry 1980; 136:26-32.
11. Folstein MF. McHugh PR. Neuropsychiatry of some specific brain disorders. In: Lades MH. Handbook of psychiatry 2: Mental disorders and somatic illness. New York: Cambridge University Press. 1983; 107-10.
12. Gilhooly, M. The impact of caregiving on caregivers: Factors associated with the psychological well-being of people supporting a dementing relative in the community. Br. J. Psychiatry 1984; 57:35-44.
13. Lawerence MK. Dealing with the difficult older patient. Can. Med. Assoc. J. 1986; 134:1122-26.
14. Hachiniski V. Cerebral blood flow: Differentiation of Alzheimer's Disease from multi-infarct dementia. In: Katzman R. Terry RD, Bick KL. eds. Alzheimer's Disease: Senile Dementia and Related Disorder. New York: Raven Press. 1978.

Dementia: A systematic approach to identifying reversible causes

BARRY REISBERG, MD

HIGHLIGHTS

The development of FAST is of great importance to clinicians in identifying possibly remediable complictions of Alzheimer's disease and distinguishing them from the characteristic progression of the illness.

Premature loss of speech in an otherwise uncomplicated Alzheimer's-type presentation should lead the clinician to strongly suspect focal cerebral pathology, especially cerebral infarction.

Our study of Alzheimer's disease (AD) patients over the past several years has yielded a rapid, practical diagnostic tool: Functional Assessment Staging of Alzheimer's Disease. We refer to this expeditious procedure as FAST staging.[1,2] FAST enables the clinician to readily accomplish the following previously difficult or impossible tasks in assessment of the aged patient with cognitive impairment:

- Determine rapidly whether the nature of the dementia is consistent with uncomplicated senile dementia of the Alzheimer's type* in its present manifestation, as well as in its evolution.

- Stage, in a relatively detailed fashion, even the most severe AD patients.

Dr. Reisberg is clinical director of the Geriatric Study and Treatment Program at New York University Medical Center, New York, and associate professor of psychiatry at the New York University School of Medicine.

- Differentiate various, sometimes treatable complications of AD from natural progression of the illness.

- Accomplish all of the above with sufficient facility that preliminary determinations regarding diagnosis, differential diagnosis, and complicating factors can be made on the basis of information provided by family members (in many cases, even over the telephone) before actual examination of the patient.

Although the neuropathology and pathophysiology of dementia of the Alzheimer's type, which have been studied extensively,[6,7] are well known, the clinical progression of AD has not been studied as extensively. Consequently, physicians often find clinical differentiation from other dementias exceedingly difficult. It is also difficult for clinicians to distinguish which symptoms are inevitable with disease progression and which are due to other possibly treatable causes.

Clinicians need a means to describe

• In the psychiatric nomenclature, the current terminology for this disease entity is "primary degenerative dementia."[3] A National Institute of Neurologic Diseases and Stroke and Alzheimer's Disease and Related Disorders Association workshop recently suggested the term "probable Alzheimer's disease" for this condition.[4] The Secretary's Task Force on Alzheimer's Disease of the US Department of Health and Human Services in a September 1984 report[5] referrred to this disorder simply as "Alzheimer's disease," a convention that shall be used in this paper.

the anticipated time course and progression of AD in terms understandable to both patients and colleagues. Development of a practical tool to accomplish these tasks was possible for several reasons:

- AD is a pervasive dementing process the progression of which has a definable consistency;

- Dementing processes associated with other causes proceed differently than AD and

- Since many functional activities in all 20th-century societies are universal, functional decrements can be described in universal – ie. generally understandable – terms.

The FAST stages of progressive AD are numbered to correspond with the Global Deterioration Scale (GDS) stages of normal aging to facilitate comparison.[8] The FAST stages, their long-term prognostic concomitants[9] and their application are described below. These procedures can provide an invaluable supplement to the general dementia workup[10] which should also be conducted in all patients with cognitive deterioration of uncertain etiology.

Stage 1

No objective or subjective functional decrement. The aged subject's objective and subjective functional abilities in occupational, social, and other settings remain intact, compared with performance 5 to 10 years previously.

Diagnosis. Normal cognitive functioning.

Prognosis. Excellent for continued adequate cognitive functioning.

Stage 2

Subjective functional decrement, but no objective evidence of decrease performance in complex occupational or social activities. The most common age-related functional complaints are forgetting names and location of objects and decreased ability to recall appointments. Subjective decrements are generally not noted by intimates or coworkers, and complex occupational and social functioning is not compro mised.

Alzheimer's disease

Diagnosis. Cognitive functioning compatible with normal aging.

Prognosis. Excellent for continued adequate cognitive functioning.

Commentary. Subjective symptoms are very common in elderly persons. They may be troubling and may lead the person to consult a physician. The symptoms may be associated with primary affective disorders or primary anxiety, and symptoms of these conditions should be looked for carefully. In many cases, no condition other than normal aging is found.

Treatment implications. When affective disorders, anxiety states, or other remediable conditions have been excluded, the elderly person with these symptoms can be reassured with respect to the relatively benign prognosis. This reassurance may alleviate fears in the patient that the symptoms presage a malignant deterioration, which, in the great majority of cases, they do not.

Stage 3

Objective functional decrement of sufficient severity to interfere with complex occupational and social tasks. This is the stage at which persons may begin to forget important appointments for the first time in their lives. Similarly a professional person who may have been able to write hundreds of articles or reports over the course of his or her adult years now, for the first time, finds it impossible to finish a single report.

Functional decrements may also become manifest in complex psychomotor tasks, such as ability to travel to new locations. Persons at this stage have no difficulty with routine tasks such as shopping, handling finances, or traveling to familiar locations. they may stop participating in demanding occupational and social settings, whereupon their deficits may no longer be manifest.

Diagnosis. Cognitive functioning compatible with borderline functioning secondary to a variety of possible conditions, including subtle manifestations of psychiatric, neurologic, or medical pathology, or incipient AD.

Prognosis. The 3 to 4-year prognosis appears to be benign with respect to further cognitive deterioration n more than 80% of cases.

Commentary. Although clinically these symptoms may appear subtle, they can considerably alter lifestyle. They can be sufficiently alarming as to result in an emergency visit to a physician or clinic.

Treatment implications. When psychiatric, neurologic, and medical concomitants apart from AD have been excluded, the physician might counsel a "tactical withdrawal" from situations that have become, by virtue of their complexity, anxiety-provoking. Since patients at this stage can still perform all basic activities of daily living satisfactorily, withdrawing from complex activities may result in complete symptom amelioration for a period of years.

Stage 4

Deficient performance in the complex tasks of daily life. At this stage, persons have difficulty returning from shopping with the correct items and proper amounts of foodstuffs and other materials. Unless supervised, they have difficulty balancing their checkbooks and may make significant financial errors. Functioning in other complex areas is also compromised.

A pair of brief case histories illustrates this: One patient scheduled a dinner party and instructed one-half of the guests to arrive on a particular day and the other guests to arrive on the following day. Another patient at this stage ostensibly continued to function as an attorney in partnership with the spouse. Although the patient was able to independently travel to and from the office daily, when queried, neither the names nor details of any cases supposedly being worked on could be recalled. In actuality, the spouse had taken on the patient's caseload.

Patients at this stage can still function independently in the community, since they can dress, bathe, choose their own clothing, and travel to familiar locations. However, such functioning is compromised, as in the case of the patient at this stage who resided alone, continued to pay rent personally, but, when queried, underestimated the amount of the rent by 50%. The same patient incorrectly described the residence as a hotel, when it was actually an apartment house.

Diagnosis. Cognitive functioning consistent with mild AD.

Prognosis. If properly and carefully diagnosed cases only are considered, and if one excludes questionable cases, then none of these patients ever shows recovery of former abilities. A significant minority – 27% in our series – do not demonstrate notable decline, however, over the subsequent 3- to 4-year interval. Another 27% of our patients at this stage were deceased at follow-up, and an equal percentage were institutionalized. The remaining subjects (approximately 18% in our series) continued to reside in the community 3 to 4 years later, although their clinical status had notably deteriorated.

Commentary. Many patients continue to function independently in a community setting, although their symptoms may lead to financial and other difficulties.

Family members may become alarmed by the symptoms at this stage and may bring the patient to the physician for diagnosis for the first time. An unusually stressful situation may result in increased anxiety in these patients and, occasionally, an emergency visit.

Treatment implications. The physician should work with the family toward the goal of maximizing the patient's functioning. Financial supervision should be arranged. Structured and/or supervised travel should also be arranged. Identification bracelets and address labels sewn into the clothing may be useful.

In most cases, denial protects the patient against what would otherwise be the devastating emotional consequences of the memory loss at this stage.[11]

Stage 5

Deficient performance in such basic tasks of daily life as choosing proper clothing. Patients can no longer function independently. The caregiver must assist not only in managing financial affairs and in shopping, but also must assist the patient in choosing the proper clothing for the season and the occasion. The patient will frequently wear obviously incongruous clothing combinations unless the caregiver intervenes. Indeed, this deficit in choosing proper clothing is virtually pathognomonic of this stage.

Less characteristically, some patients begin to forget to bathe regularly unless reminded. Sometimes coaxing as well as reminding to bathe is necessary.

Patients at this stage are still capable of putting on their clothing properly, once it has been selected for them. They are also capable of bathing themselves and even of adjusting the bath water properly when washing, although, as mentioned, they may have been cajoled or reminded to bathe.

Another functional deficit that frequently becomes manifest over the course of this stage is difficulty driving an automobile. The patient may inappropriately speed up and slow down the vehicle, mistakenly go through stop sign or stop light, or even collided with another vehicle for the first time in many years.

Frequently, the patient is sufficiently alarmed by these deficits as to voluntarily discontinue driving.

Occasionally, coercion from the spouse or other caregiver is necessary.
Diagnosis. Cognitive functioning consistent with moderate AD.

Prognosis. A minority of patients, even at this stage, do not show deterioration over the subsequent 3- to 4-year interval. Most, however, either are found to be deceased, institutionalized, or if in the community, deteriorated.

Commentary. Crying episodes or other emotional disturbances, including hyperactivity and a variation in diurnal rhythm (sleep disturbance), frequently result in crises and physician intervention at this stage.

Treatment implications. The patient can no longer survive independently in a community setting. The physician should discuss with the caregiver the desirability of additional part-time homemaker or other assistance. Daycare programs may be useful for the patient, and continuous support groups for the caregiver. Driving becomes hazardous, and should be discontinued. The caregiver may

TABLE 1

FAST symptomatology and differential diagnostic considerations

FAST characteristics	FAST stage	DDx considerations, particularly if FAST stage occurs early (non-ordinally) in evolution of dementia
No functional decrement subjectively or objectively	1	
Complains of forgetting locations of objects Subjective work difficulties	2	Anxiety neurosis Depression
Decreased functioning in demanding work settings evident to co-workers Difficulty travelling to new locations	3	Depression Subtle manifestations of medical pathology
Decreased ability to perform complex tasks (eg, planning dinner party, shopping, personal finances)	4	Depression Psychosis Focal cerebral process (eg, Gerstmann syndrome)
Requires assistance selecting attire May require coaxing to bathe properly	5	Depression
Difficulty dressing properly	6a	Arthritis • Sensory deficit • Stroke • Depression
Requires assistance bathing, fear of bathing	b	(Same as 6a)
Difficulty with mechanics of toileting	c	(Same as 6a)
Urinary incontinence	d	Urinary tract infection Other causes of urinary incontinence
Fecal incontinence	e	Infection Malabsorption syndrome Other causes of fecal incontinence
Vocabulary limited to 1 to 5 words	7a	Stroke Other dementing disorder (eg, diffuse space-occupying lesions)
Intelligible vocabulary lost	b	(Same as 7a)
Ambulatory ability lost	c	Parkinsonism Neuroleptic-induced or other secondary extrapyramidal syndrome Creutzfeldt-Jakob disease Normal pressure hydrocephalus Hyponatremic dementia Stroke • Hip fracture • Arthritis • Overmedication
Ability to sit lost	d	Arthritis • Contractures
Ability to smile lost	e	Stroke
Ability to hold up head lost	f	Head trauma Metabolic abnormality • Overmedication Encephalitis • Other causes
Ultimately, stupor or coma		

Source: Author

require guidance in handling the patient's emotional outbursts. Less frequently, psychotropic medication may be useful in treating anxiety, depression, or psychosis associated with AD, at this stage.

Stage 6

Decreased ability to dress, bathe, and toilet independently. In uncomplicated AD, these three functional deficits usually proceed in sequence with the evolution of the illness. Five distinct, sequential functional substages can be identified that allow the physician and caregiver to anticipate the course of the illness.

It should be noted that distinctions between these substages may be less marked than those between the major functional stages. Hence, stages 6a and 6b may be evident simultaneously, or in uncomplicated AD, the progressive functional-deficit substages may not occur in sequence. For example, stage 6b may precede 6a.

Substage 6a: Decreased ability to put on clothing properly. Initially, many patients put their daytime clothing on over their nightclothes. Other patients will, for the first time in their adult lives, experience difficulty tying shoelaces or putting shoes on the proper feet. As the illness advances, increasing assistance from caregivers is needed to help the patients clothe themselves properly.

Substage 6b: Decreased ability to bathe independently. Ability to properly adjust the bath water, enter and exit the bath, wash properly, and completely dry oneself declines. As noted above, fear or resistance sometimes precedes actual deficits in bathing.

Substage 6c: Decreased ability to perform mechanics of toileting independently. Patients at this stage begin to forget to flush the toilet. They also may begin to forget to wipe themselves when toileting, and may develop difficulty in pulling up their underclothing or trousers. The caregiver begins to assist the patient in handling the mechanics of toileting.

Substage 6d: Urinary incontinence. Occasionally this occurs virtually simultaneously with stage 6c, but more frequently, there is a discernable interval of a few to several months between these substages. The urinary incontinence occurs at this stage in the absence of infection or other genitourinary tract pathology. It appears to be entirely the result of decreased cognitive capacity to respond to urinary urgency with appropriate toileting behavior.

Substage 6e: Fecal incontinence. Fecal and urinary incontinence may occur simultaneously or even at the same time that difficulties with the mechanics of toileting become evident. More frequently, this substage is temporally discrete. The mechanism appears to be identical to that of urinary incontinence; ie, decreased cognitive capacity.

Diagnosis. Cognitive functioning consistent with moderately severe AD.

Prognosis. Most patients followed at this stage are institutionalized or decreased at the time of the follow-up after approximately 4 years.

Commentary. Agitation and overt psychotic symptoms often produce crises that result in medical contact. Other symptoms, such as onset of incontinence, may also produce crises. Violence and/or incontinence may lead the family to consider institutionalization for the patient.

Treatment implications. The physician should assist the caregivers in assessing the degree of additional home care assistance that may be necessary. Full-time home health care assistance is frequently useful at this stage. Strategies for assisting with bathing and toileting, and for managing incontinence should be discussed with the family. Many patients at this stage develop agitation, paranoia, and/or delusions, which respond to appropriate, low-dosage neuroleptic intervention. The physician should attempt to minimize emotional stress in the caregiver with supportive techniques. In certain cases, institutionalization should be discussed with the family or other caregivers.

Stage 7

Loss of speech, locomotion, and consciousness. This is the final stage of AD. Although some Alzheimer's patients succumb earlier in the course of the illness to social hazards (eg. vehicular accidents, assaults, becoming hopelessly lost, or infections (for which persons with decrease cognitive capacity have an increase susceptibility), the majority of AD patients survive until some point in the seventh stage. Again, a number of substages afford the the clinician and family some predictive capability.

Substage 7a: Vocabulary becomes limited to fewer than a half-dozen words. Deficits in vocabulary and speech abilities increase with progression of AD. Reticence and a paucity of speech are frequently noted in the fourth and fifth GDS stages. In the sixth stage, the ability to speak in complete sentences is gradually lost. After the development of incontinence, speech becomes even more circumscribed to single words or short phrases, and spoken vocabulary becomes limited to only a few words.

Substage 7b: Intelligible vocabulary becomes limited to a single word. The final spoken word for the AD patient varies. For some patients, the spoken vocabulary becomes limited to the single word "yes". For other patients the final spoken word is "no". For one of our patients, the final word was "okay", which was repeated in response to all verbalization-provoking phenomena, including need to toilet, express anxiety, and express either the affirmative or the negative.

As illness progresses, the ability to speak even this final single word is lost. However, months afterward, the patient may suddenly articulate the seemingly forgotten final word, only to return to a state of obliviousness with respect to intelligible speech. After intelligible speech is lost, vocalizations become limited to grunts or screams.

Substage 7c: Loss of ambulatory ability. Neuropathologic studies indicate that the motor cortex is spared except in the most severe (late) stages of AD. Perhaps this late cortical deterioration accounts for the loss of ambulatory ability at this late point in the evolution of the disease.

It should be noted, however, that lesser forms of ambulatory disturbance are not uncommon at earlier stages. These less severe locomotor disturbances may be the result of decreased cognitive capacities, and resultant psychomotor changes, rather than destruction of the motor cortex per se. For example, inappropriate gait speed (the patient either walks too quickly or too slowly) is not infrequently noted in the earlier stages of the disease. In the sixth stage, the patient may begin to ambulate more deliberately or to take smaller steps. Assistance in walking up and down staircases is generally required prior to the loss of all ambulatory ability.

The onset of ambulatory loss during stage 7 is somewhat varied. Some patients simply take progressively smaller and slower steps. Others begin to tilt forward, backward, or laterally when ambulating. Twisted gaits have also been noted. After ambulatory abilities are lost, other voluntary motoric abilities become compromised.

Substage 7d: *Loss of ability to sit.* After AD patients have lost the ability to ambulate without – and subsequently even with – assistance, they

TABLE 2

Correspondence of functional assessment stages in AD to normal human development

FAST stage	Characteristics	Clinical Dx	Estimated duration in AD*	Approximate age at which function is acquired
1	No decrement	Normal adult	50 years	Adult
2	Subjective deficit in word finding	Normal aged adult	15 years	
3	Deficits noted in demanding employment settings	Compatible incipient AD	7 years	Young adult
4	Require assistance in complex tasks, such as handling finances, planning dinner party	Mild AD	2 years	8 years to adolescence
5	Requires assistance in choosing proper attire	Moderate AD	18 months	5 to 7 years
6a	Requires assistance dressing	Moderately severe AD	5 months	5 years†
b	Requires assistance bathing properly	(same as 6a)	5 months	4 years†
c	Requires assistance with mechanics of toileting (eg, flushing, wiping)	(same as 6a)	5 months	48 months‡
d	Urinary incontinence	(same as 6a)	4 months	36 to 54 months§
e	Fecal incontinence	(same as 6a)	10 monts	24 to 36 months†‡§
7a	Speech ability limited to about a half-dozen intelligible words	Severe AD	12 months	15 months†‡
b	Intelligible vocabulary limited to single word	(same as 7a)	18 months	12 months†‡
c	Ambulatory ability lost	(same as 7a)	12 months	12 months†‡
d	Ability to sit up lost	(same as 7a)	12 months	24 to 40 weeks†‡
e	Ability to smile lost	(same as 7a)	18 months	8 to 16 weeks†‡
f	Ability to hold up head lost	(same as 7a)	Not applicable	4 to 12 weeks†‡

* In subjects who survive and progress to the subsequent deterioration stage
† Eisenberg[19]
‡ Vaughn[20]
§ Pierce[21]

Source: Author

are still capable of sitting in a chair unassisted. Approximately 1 year after ambulatory ability is lost, the ability to sit up unassisted is lost. At this point, they are still capable of smiling, chewing, grunting, crying out, and grasping.

Substage 7e: Loss of ability to smile. At this stage, AD survivors can generally still move their eyes and may appear to show deliberate ocular movements in response to stimuli, however, they no longer recognize familiar persons or objects. Grasp reflexive ability is also preserved, as is the ability to swallow and even to chew in many patients. Also, patients at this stage continue to cry out in response to stimuli.

Substage 7f: Loss of ability to hold up the head. The few AD patients who survive to this point may need to be fed with a pipette, in part because of their decreased capacity to recognize food. They may still make noises, but these vocalizations are not readily associated with exogenous stimuli.

Prognosis. Since AD is not generally noted on death certificates as a cause of death, a certain circularity occurs with respect to the demise of Alzheimer's victims. Since AD cannot be the "cause", another cause is ascribed. Nevertheless, a recent study of Sulkava et al,[12] indicated that 14% (3 of 22) of the AD patients followed to autopsy ultimately died of no obvious immediate cause other than AD, "suggesting a failure in the central regulation of vital functions, such as respiration."

Commentary. As AD patients are increasingly well cared for, it is likely that more will survive to these final substages of the illness, and that the illness beyond this point will be increasingly well described.

Treatment implications. Full-time assistance in a community or institutional setting is a necessity at this stage. Strategies for locomotion, feeding, and other activities of daily living should be discussed with the caregiver. Soft-food diets are generally tolerated; however, nasogastric feeding may be necessary during crises. The need for psychotropic medication frequently disappears. The most frequent causes of death and disability to be avoided are aspiration pneumonia and traumatic or decubital ulceration.

FAST: Utility in staging severe dementia

Viewing the progression of Alzheimer's disease in this systematic way allows us to track the disease beyond the capability of currently available formal instruments. More specifically; at the stage at which Alzheimer's victims lose the ability to dress themselves (6a), they may, for reasons related to behavioral disturbance as well as to cognitive deficit, achieve only baseline (zero) scores on most psychometrics and even mental status evaluations. Hence, such tests may be less useful in differentiating patients from this point on. At the point when patents lose the ability to speak (early part of FAST stage 7), psychometrics tests and mental status assessments are uniformly of no value in the further differentiation of patients according to the magnitude of severity of the illness process.

On the other hand, FAST staging of AD enables us to expeditiously distinguish at least 16 stages, many of which lie beyond the point at which other available assessment procedures fail to be informative.

Although the importance of this FAST staging capacity to AD research is difficult to overestimate, of equal clinical significance is the utility of the FAST in enabling clinicians to identify possibly remediable complications and anticipate disease progression until death ensues.

FAST: Utility in differential diagnosis

In conjunction with information about onset, course, and presentation of AD, FAST staging is of great value in diagnosis of uncomplicated AD. FAST staging is also very valuable in assisting the clinician in identifying extraneous treatable complications of AD – distinguishing them from signs of characteristic AD progression. Additionally, FAST staging facilitates differential diagnosis of AD from other dementing disorders of the middle-aged and elderly (table 1).

Identifying common treatable complications of AD. The following are examples of how FAST staging can assist in the proper diagnosis of an otherwise obscure picture when illnesses complicate an apparently consistent Alzheimer's clinical presentation:

- Inability to shop or handle finances at the time when a person can still function adequately in a demanding employment setting should lead the clinician to consider the possibility of a focal cerebral process associated with, for example, acalculia or a "pseudodementing" process such as depression.

- Inability to put on clothing properly at the time when a patient can still choose the proper clothing to wear can occur in depression. It can also, of course, occur as a result of cerebral focal pathology, such as that caused by a stroke or CNS metastasis. Arthritis, a fracture, or other physically debilitative processes can also result in this presentation.

- Inability to handle mechanics of bathing when the AD patient is still capable of choosing the proper clothing for the season and occasion commonly results from arthritis or other physical disabilities.

- Development of urinary incontinence before the anticipated numerical stage might indicate a urinary tract infection, which might respond to appropriate intervention with antimicrobial agents.

- Development of fecal incontinence before the anticipated numerical stage might indicate a gastrointestinal infection. It might also indicate one of the numerous other possible causes of incontinence in the elderly, which should be investigated in an appropriate fashion.

- Premature loss of speech in an otherwise uncomplicated Alzheimer's – type presentation should lead the clinician to strongly suspect focal cerebral pathology, especially cerebral infarction. Loss of speech might thus be indicative of multi-infarct dementia or mixed degenerative dementia and infarction.

It should be noted that cerebral infarction may occur even in the absence of evidence of infarction on CT study. A magnetic resonance

Case history 1: Progessive functional loss in uncomplicated AD

In 1974, Mrs. T was a 51-year-old, happily married mother of two children who had been working full time in New York as a book-keeper, That year she became increasingly "confused," and this confusion resulted in her leaving her job. Her family recalls that subsequently she had difficulty reading and "became less involved with her environment." Specifically, she developed difficulty knitting and lost interest in performing household chores.

When she and her husband moved to Florida in 1978, Mrs. T reacted negatively to the move. She was taken first to a therapist for treatment of her "negative reaction," then to a neurologist. In the fall of 1978, the neurologist diagnosed AD.

I evaluated her for the first time in July 1982, at which time she demonstrated moderately severe to severe (stage 5 to 6) memory impairment in most areas assessed. For example, she did not know the month of the year, but did give the season as "into summer." She could not remember where she had been married, but did recall the names of her primary and secondary schools. She did not know her current address or the city in which she resided, but with reflection, was able to recall the President's name. She was unable to count backward from 20 by 2's, but was able to count from 10 backward by 1's. Functionally, she was noted to occasionally put her blouse on backward and put her shoes on the wrong feet, and remain unaware of anything amiss. She also manifested some difficulty in choosing silverware properly. Functionally, I estimated she was in the early sixth stage, specifically, 6a.

Approximately a year later, in May 1983, I reevaluated her and found no notable overall decline. Functionally, she was having difficulty bathing as well as putting on her clothing. Her husband had found it necessary to begin adjusting her bathwater temperature. She was assessed at stage 6b. In May 1984, her functioning had deteriorated to the point where she would forget to flush the toilet unless reminded; a year later, in July 1985, functionally she was still at the point where she could not handle toileting without some assistance. Although we might anticipate that the next problem will be incontinence, this had not yet developed in July 1985; there were no urinary or fecal accidents. She had no idea of the season, month, or year, but knew her own name and, occasionally, her husband's name.

TABLE 3

Case history 1: Progressive functional deficits in uncomplicated AD

FAST Stage	Year	Observed functional deficit
3	1974	Unable to continue working as bookkeeper
4	1978	Difficulty performing household chores
5	1978-82	Difficulty choosing proper clothing
6a	July 1982	Difficulty dressing independently
b	May 1983	Difficulty bathing independently
c	May 1984-May 1985	Difficulty with mechanics of toileting

Source: Author

As would be expected from her functional stage and the fact that her disease was not complicated by other illnesses, Mrs. T was still capable not only of continence, but of speaking in sentences and ambulating without assistance. She could recall neither her elementary school nor her high school, but could give her parents' names. She also recalled she had been born in Brooklyn. Mrs. T could not tell me her address, the nature of the weather that day, or recall the name of the current President. However, when I said "Ronald," she was able to respond "Reagan." She had difficulty counting forward from 1 to 10.

Commentary. From 1974 through 1985, the functional decrements in Mrs. T's case developed sequentially precisely as would be anticipated in a case of uncomplicated AD. The actual time intervals of progression (table 3) are, of course, gross approximations. As such, these intervals, in this case, bear some relationship to the approximated expected intervals for uncomplicated AD (table 2). This course might be expected to vary; in this case, for example, depending in part upon the point in the third stage at which the patient's illness was identified. The entire anticipated interval is about 12 years, which is very close to the observed course in this particular case.

BARRY REISBERG, MD

imaging (MRI) study may occasionally reveal a large or small infarction that is entirely invisible on the CT.[13] In any event, MRI may be particularly useful in differentiating senile dementia of the Alzheimer's type from multi-infarct dementia and mixed degenerative and infarction dementias.[14]

Even in the absence of any neuroradiologic evidence for infarction, either on CT or MRI, the clinician should carefully search for other evidence of focal pathology, such as asymmetric reflexes or other asymmetric sensory or motor abilities. Such asymmetry can help confirm suspicion of focal phenomena in, for example, an Alzheimer's patient who may be incapable of toileting without some assistance, but who is still continent and who has recently lost all ability to utter intelligible speech.

- Premature loss of ambulatory ability in otherwise uncomplicated AD may be due to cerebral infarction; CNS metastatic disease; other primary causes of dementia, including

Case history 2: Progessive functional loss in demential of other etiology

Mrs. W. was, in September 1983, a 69-year-old married woman and the mother of three adult children; she resided in an apartment house in Brooklyn.

Her medical history included a series of 20 electroconvulsive therapy treatments that were administered in an outpatient setting over an 8-month period in 1962 and 1963. As her family recalled, these were given for a "fear complex" and "crying spells", both of which improved following the treatments. No antidepressant medication was prescribed, and there were no further episodes of affective disorder.

Shortly afterward, she was noted to be hypertensive and was treated for the subsequent 20 years for this condition. From approximately 1974 onward, she took clonidine HCl, 0.2 mg tid, and 25 mg hydrochlorothiazide/50 mg triamterene once daily. Her most recent BP was 130/80 mm Hg.

In 1978 she was noted to be diabetic and was placed on chlorpropamide, 250 mg/d, which she took regularly thereafter.

In 1981, visual disturbances and difficulty reading and sewing became apparent. Bilateral macular degeneration was diagnosed, and Mrs. W. received laser treatments for this condition in October 1983. Her vision remained poor, however, and her hearing began to deteriorate at this time. Her surgical history was notable only for a left-sided oophorectomy 41 years previously.

In September 1983, Mrs. W. complained of pain and "numbness" in her femoral region that prevented her from walking. A fracture at L1 was discovered and apparently successfully treated with immobilization. Tests at that time revealed a slightly lowered serum sodium.

Over the next 5 months, Mrs. W. deteriorated markedly. Her appetite declined and her weight went from 180 to 140 lbs. She complained of forgetfulness, and her family also noted a disturbance in Mrs. W's. ability to remember. She cried continuosly "for 2 weeks". In February 1984, she developed "visions" that her family had noted for 1 to 2 weeks before admission. Her family also noted various somatic complaints such as her "eyes burning".

At this time, Mrs. W's general practitioner, who had been caring for her for the past 20years, added imipramine HCl, 50 mg hs. to the chlorpropamide (250 mg/d) and the clonidine (0.2 mg tid) that she had been receiving. He performed B12, folate, and thyroid studies, all of which were normal. He also referred her to a neurologist in another county who did EEG and CT, as well as serum studies. The neurologist diagnosed AD and conveyed his findings to the local physician who, in turn, suggested that the family seek nursing home placement.

The family, particularly Mrs. W's. children, was very distressed. They contacted the Alzheimer's Disease and Related Disorders Association headquarters in Chicago, which, in turn, suggested a support group and referred the children to our program at NYU. The son called me to inquire about support groups. He said he and his sisters did not know how they were going to live with his mother's illness. I asked him to tell me a little about his mother's inability to talk, her affective component, and the history of electroconvulsive therapy treatments, diabetes, and hypertension.

notably Creutzfeldt – Jakob disease, normal-pressure hydrocephalus, or metabolic dementias; hip or leg fractures; arthritis; severe peripheral vascular disease; primary or secondary parkinsonism; or over-medication.

- Development of a comatose state in an Alzheimer's patient may occur from many causes. Those that should be prominently considered include over-medication, inter-current illness, a cerebrovascular accident, and head trauma. Head trauma can lead to unconsciousness and apparent "foaming at the mouth," which can be mistaken for a seizure.

Alzheimer's: Normal functional development reversed

The hierarchical nature of the clinical symptoms in AD has been noted by at least two groups of independent investigators.[15,16] De Ajuriaguerra, et al[17] hypothesized in 1964 that the deficits in senile dementia represent a reversal of Piaget's human developmental stages. Our functional observations, when viewed retrospectively, appear to be in agreement with this hypothesis (table 2).[18,21]

In other ways, AD deficits are not analogous, in reverse order, to normal development. Clearly, the somatic gains in human development are not

He also told me that his mother had been definitely diagnosed and that the family was looking for a nursing home. I suggested that the history – notably the rapid onset and the inability to walk, along with the preservation of speech – did not sound, over the telephone, compatible with AD. When I strongly suggested that his mother be seen for a consultation, he replied that she could not walk and could not be moved, and hence could not be brought to see me. Sensing the urgency of the situation and despite some logistic difficulties, I agreed to conduct a home visit.

When I arrived, in Feb.1984, I obtained the above history. I also found a woman moaning in bed with a severe (stage 6) memory disturbance. Functionally, she demonstrated disability in all assessments corresponding to stage 6c. She also was unable to ambulate (stage 7c), but was not incontinent, and could articulate sentences. The family insisted that the L1 fracture had healed and that Mrs. W's inability to walk was due to "weakness".

Cognitively, she had difficulty counting backward from 10 to 1; gave the current president as "Roosevelt"; did not know her own telephone number; told me she was born in "Europe, Alaska"; could not tell me the name of the high school or primary school she attended; and gave the year as "15". She was able to count from 1 to 10, knew her current street address; and knew her parents' names, as well as her own name and those of her children. In summary, her deficits were consistent with stage 6 Alzheimer's disease, but that was apart from the inability to walk and the too-rapid onset.

My bedside diagnosis included:
- endogenous depression;
- hyponatremia;
- mild hypertension;
- mild diabetes;
- macular degeneration; and
- decrease audition.

I strongly urged immediate hospitalization at NYU.

The patient was hospitalized the next day. Her serum sodium was 119 mEq/L. This was believed to be secondary to both the hydrochlorothiazide/triamterene and the chlorpropamide. These were discontinued. The hypertension was stabilized without medication, and tolbutamide was utilized in place of the chlorpropamide. As the serum sodium increased, there was an immediate improvement in cognition. Over the next month, cognition returned to near normal at the time of discharge. Subsequently, over the next several months cognition returned to normal.

Commentary. Metabolic dementias, severe depression, stroke, encephalitis, and other conditions, such as normal pressure hydrocephalus, can all result in dementia accompanied by, what would be for an Alzheimer's patient, early loss of ambulatory ability. The gross deviation from the expected sequential progression (table 1) can sometimes be evident, as in Mrs. W's case – even in the course of brief telephone conversation.

Even if a non-Alzheimer's dementia mimics AD in its functional progression, it is unlikely to follow the anticipated duration of the sequential stages (table 2). In Mrs. W's case, the estimated 5-month progression from apparent normality to an apparent FAST stage of at least 6c (if we discount the ambulatory loss) was clearly too rapid for uncomplicated AD.

BARRY REISBERG, MD

paralleled by somatic losses in AD. Also, the emotional changes in Alzheimer's disease, as described elsewhere in greater detail,[22,23] are not analogous, generally, to human emotional growth.

The cognitive changes of AD, however, apparently do occur in reverse order to gains in these areas in normal human development. Briefly, the deficits in AD reflect bilateral cortical degeneration, just as the gains in normal human development are largely the result of cortical maturation.

Conclusion

In what we now recognize to have been the seminal description of the clinical syndrome of AD, Benjamin Rush, in his 1793 psychiatric text, described a patient "who exhibited the marks of second infancy, by such a total decay of mental faculties as to lose all consciousness in discharging her alvine and urinary excretions."[24] It appears the first portion of this description with respect to a "second infancy" was as accurate as the latter, which refers to the double incontinence that develops at a point in the evolution of dementia of the Alzheimer's type.

Until only recently, little more in the way of clinical description was added to Rush's brief synopsis. It is now possible, however, to sketch the clinical course of AD in universal, readily discernible terms.

Clinicians can use these descriptions in everyday practice to differentiate this very common dementing disorder from dementia of other etiology. Having made the diagnosis of AD, its course can be predicted with some accuracy, and potentially treatable complications can be distinguished from the natural progression of the disorder. (see Case history 1: Progressive functional loss in uncomplicated AD, page 43, and Case history 2: Progressive functional loss in dementia of other etiology, page 44.) The brief, practical functional staging procedure described here can accomplish these tasks with optimal facility.

Address reprint requests to Barry Reisberg, MD, Clinical Director, Geriatric Study and Treatment Program, New Yprk University Medical Center, 550 First Avenue, New York, NY 10016.

References

1. Reisberg B. Ferris SH. Anand R. et al. Functional staging of dementia of the Alzheimer's type. Ann NY Acad. Sci. 1984; 435:481-3.

2. Reisberg B. Ferris SH. Franssen E. An ordinal functional assessment tool for Alzheimer's – type dementia. Hosp. Community Psychiatry 1985; 36:593-5.

3. American Psychiatric Association. Diagnostic and statistical manual of mental disorders. 3d ed. Washington. DC: American Psychiatric Association, 1983.

4. McKhann G. Drachman D. Folstein M. Katzman R. Price D. Stadlan EM. Clinical diagnosis of Alzheimer's disease: Report of the NINCDS-ADRDA Work Group under the auspices of Department of Health and Human Serivices Task Force on Alzheimer's disease. Neurology (Cleveland) 1983; 34:939-44.

5. US Department of Health and Human Services, Alzheimer's disease: report of the secretary's task force on Alzheimer's disease. US Government Printing Office, 1984.

6. Schneck MK. Reisberg B. Ferris SH. An overview of current concepts of Alzheimer's disease. Am J. Psychiatry 1982; 134:165-73.

7. Reisberg B. ed. Alzheimer's disease. New York: Free Press/Macmillan, 1983.

8. Reisberg B. Ferris SH. de Leon MJ. Crook T. The global deterioration scale for asessment of primary degenerative dementia. Am J. Psychiatry 1982; 139:1136-9.

9. Reisberg B. Ferris SH. Schulman E. et al. Longitudinal course of normal aging and progressive dementia of the Alzheimer's type: a prospective study of 106 subjects over a 3.6 year mean interval. Prog. Neuropsychopharmacol Biol. Psychiatry (in press).

10. Reisberg B. Ferris SH. Diagnosis and assessment of the older patient. Hosp. Community Psychiatry 1982; 33:104-10.

11. Reisberg B. Gordon B. McCarthy M. Ferris SH. de Leon MJ. Insight and denial accompanying progressive cognitive decline in normal aging and Alzheimer's disease. In: Stanley B. ed. Geriatric psychiatry: ethical and legal issues. Washington DC: American Psychiatric Press. 1985; 37-79.

12. Sulkava R. Haltia M. Paetau A. Wilkstrom J. Palo J. Accuracy of clinical diagnosis in primary degenerative dementia: correlation with neuropathological findings. J. Neurol Neurosurg Psychiatry 1983; 46:9-13.

13. Sipponen JT. Kaste M. Seppnen RE. Kuurne T. Suoranta H. Sivula A. Nuclear magnetic resonance imaging in reversible cerebral ischemia. Lancet 1983; 1:294-5.

14. Besson JAO. Corrigan FM. Foreman EI. Ashcrof. Gw. EAstwood I.M. Smith FW. Differentiating senile dementia of Alzheimer type and multi-infarct dementia by proton NMR imaging. Lancet 1983;2:789.

15. Cole MG. Dastoor DP. Koszycki D. The hierarchic dementia scale. J Clin. Exp. Gerontol 1983; 5:219-34.

16. Reisberg B. Ferris Sh. Anand R. de Leon MJ. Schneck MK. Crook T. Clinical assessment of cognitive decline in normal aging and primary degenerative dementia: concordant ordinal measures. In: Pinchot P. et al. eds. Psychiatry. vol 5. New York: Plenum Press. 1985; 333-8.

17. de Ajuriaguerra J. Rey M. Bellet-Muller M. A propos de quelques problemes posees par le deficit operatoire des viellards atteints de demence degenerative en debut d'evolution. Cortex 1964; 1:232-56.

18. Reisberg B. Ferris SH. Franssen E. Functional degenerative stages in dementia of the Alzheimer's type appear to reverse normal human development. In: Shagass, et al. eds. Biological Psychiatry. Amsterdam: Elsevier (in press).

19. Eisenberg L. Normal child development. In: Fredman AM. Kaplan HR. Sadock BJ. eds. Comprehensive Textbook of Psychiatry - II. Baltimore: Williams and Wilkins, 1975: 2036-54.

20. Vaughn VC. Growth and development. In: Nelson WE. Vaughn VC. Mckay RJ. eds. Textbook of Pediatrics. 9th ed. Philadelphia: WB. Saunders, 1969: 15-57.

21. Pierce, C.M. Enuresis and encopresis. In: Freedman AM. Kaplan HR. Sadock BJ. eds. Comprehensive Textbook of Psychiatry - II. Baltimore: Williams and Wilkins. 1975: 2116-25.

22. Reisberg B. Ferris, SH. de Leon MJ. Crook T. Age-associated cognitive decline and Alzheimer's disease implications for assessment and treatment. In: Bergener M. Ermini M. Stahelin HB. eds. Thresholds in Aging. London: Academic Press, 1985: 255-92.

23. Reisberg B. Ferris SH. A clinical rating scale for symptoms of psychosis in Alzheimer's disease. Psychopharmacol Bull 1985; 21:101-4.

24. Rush B. An account of the state of the mind and body in old age. Medical inquiries and observtions, vol. 2. Philadelphia: Dobson, 1793:311.

SUGGESTED READINGS

Abraham, I.L., Buckwalter, K.C. & Neundorfer, M.M., (Eds.) (1988). *Nursing Clinics of North America*, Alzheimer's disease, 23(1).

Cohen, G.D. (1988). *The Brain in Human Aging*. New York: Springer Pub. Co.

Dobrof, R. (Ed.) (1986). *Social Work and Alzheimer's Disease: Practice issues with victims and their families*. New York: Haworth Press.

Eide, M. (1987). *Alzheimer's Disease*. Phoenix, AZ: Oryx Press.

Hayhurst, K. (1988). *Non-biomedical Aspects of Alzheimer's Disease and Related Disorders: A comprehensive bibliography, 1960-1988*. Burnaby, B.C.: Gerontology Research Centre, Simon Fraser University, Victoria, British Columbia, Canada.

Jorm, A.F. (1987). *A Guide to the Understanding of Alzheimer's Disease and Related Disorders*. Washington Square, N.Y.: New York University Press.

Ontario Advisory Council on Senior Citizens. (1986). *A Report to Honourable Ron Van Horne, Minister for Senior Citizens Affairs re: Alzheimer's Disease*. Ontario Advisory Council on Senior Citizens. Toronto: the Council.

Patrias, K. et al (Prepared by). *Differential Diagnosis of Alzheimer's and other Dementing Diseases: January 1983 through June 1987*. (1987). Bethesda, MD: U.S. Department of Health and Human Services, Public Health Service, National Institutes of Health.

Ross, M. (1987). *The Silent Epidemic: A comprehensive guide to Alzheimer's disease*. Willowdale: Hounslow Press.

Roth, M. & Iverson, L.L. (Eds.) (1986). *Alzheimer's Disease and Related Disorders*. For the British Council. London: Churchill Livingstone.

Schiff, M.R. (1989). *Alzheimer: A Canadian family resource guide*. Toronto: McGraw-Hill Ryerson.

Wurtman, R.J. et al (Eds.) (1990). *Alzheimer's Disease*. New York: Raven Press.

BioSciences Information Services. (1986). *International Bibliography of Alzheimer's Disease and Senile Dementias, 1976-1985*. Philadelphia.

INDEX

ABOUT THE AUTHOR

Arthur Olson is a professor and Chair of the Communication and Social Foundations at the University of Victoria, British Columbia, Canada.

Arthur, Aila, Randy and Ginny moved to Canada in 1977 where Randy married Sheilagh and enriched their lives with three sons who brought great joy to Aila and continue to bring joy to Arthur.

Aila, his beloved wife, was a journalist by profession, and a wife, mother, confidante and friend by avocation.

Aila K. Olson

January 12, 1992